ONCE
MORE
UPON
A
TOTEM

ILLUSTRATED BY

DOUGLAS TAIT

ONCE MORE UPON A TOTEM

CHRISTIE HARRIS

ATHENEUM
1973 NEW YORK

To the gifted people who first told these stories: the Tlingit, Haida, Tsimshian and Kwakiutl Indians of the Northwest Coast.

CONTENTS

ONCE
MORE
UPON
A
TOTEM

THE SETTING
FOR THE STORIES

The wind howled in from the wild North Pacific, snatching spray from the tops of the waves. It clattered pebbles across the beach, tossed the towering firs and cedars, and slashed rain at the magnificent, snow-capped mountains of the Northwest Coast.

But the cedar houses edging the beach stood fast behind the great family crests painted on their fronts in stark black and white, red and marine blue. And from their attendant totem poles, Eagle, Raven, Killer Whale, Wolf, Bear, Frog, Beaver, and Thunderbird kept fierce watch over the cedar dugouts drawn up along the beach, the canoes. High-prowed, smooth as the lining of a seashell, and brilliant with emblems —these were the canoes that could dare the wild west-

ern rivers, thread the wild maze of coastal islands, and
range the wild coast from Alaska to California. Un-
matched on the continent, these were the fifty-,
sixty-, seventy-foot canoes fashioned by the Lords of
the Coast.

Inside the largest, central house, a huge fire blazed
on a hearth that was white with broken clamshells.
Its flames leaped up toward the smoke hole in the
center, lighting tiers of assembled people. They flickered over the massive, carved cedar figures that held
up the roof beams and sent fantastic shadows across
screens emblazoned with the unique heraldry of the
proud Northern Nations.

Dancers waited on both sides of the fire, their cos-
tumes and bird masks colorful in the firelight. And
from the rear of the fire, ranged against the painted
crests of their host, chiefs and subchiefs and their
regal women watched in lustrous black sea-otter robes
or in patterned Chilkat mantles and crestal crowns
that were hung with ermine, ringed by sea-lion bristles, and filled with ceremonial swan down or eagle
down. Drums beat, singers chanted—the people had
come to a potlatch.

Wealthy and winter-leisured, they had come to
consult on public affairs and pay debts, as well as to
display family wealth and importance. They had
come to witness claims to great clan names and hereditary fishing stations, as well as to accept elegantly

4

decorated gifts for these services. They had come to feast. To confirm old alliances and establish new ones. To hear old tales and new songs. To see fantastic dances.

Most of all, though, they had come to reassure themselves. In a world of overwhelming mountains and forests, seas and storms and wild rivers, they had come to reassure themselves of their own worth by a display of the greatness of their heritage—a heritage expressed in songs and costumed dances, in myths and legends, and in one of the world's great art styles.

They had come too, perhaps, to remind themselves of the price of their pride. The price of their good fortune. For many of the tales were much, much more than exciting entertainment. Much, much more than a recounting of tribal history and a cherishing of ancient customs. Many were also a warning. An emotional reminder of what happened to a proud, wealthy people when it forgot to be worthy of its wealth and importance. When it failed to keep the sacred laws of life.

Here, where the salmon—like the cedar—was basic to life, every tribe had its own version of *The Prince Who Was Taken Away by the Salmon*.

And these people had come to hear theirs.

They had come to lose themselves in a whispering, shouting, leaping, gesturing version that was vivid with detail, vibrant with emotion.

5

Our version can be only a distant echo of the ancient tale that roused cries of joy and tears of understanding among those drumming, chanting, dancing, feasting people of the potlatch.

THE PRINCE WHO WAS TAKEN AWAY BY THE SALMON

It happened a long, long time ago—long before white men came to the North Pacific. Things were different then, very, very different.

Then, only winding ocean channels, rivers, and forest trails carried people through the vast wildernesses. Yaloa, a young prince of a Killer Whale clan, preferred the trails to the waterways. For it was the trails that led into the hills where the white mountain goats leaped, a challenge to hunters like his father.

Yaloa's father was the greatest hunter in the tribe, a man bounding with vigor and high spirits. He was also head chief in their upriver village.

Yaloa often looked wistfully at the emblems that were carved and painted on his father's house. For it was Eagle that topped the housepole, Eagle that spread its wings across the housefront. And Eagle was not Yaloa's totem.

In the way of the great Northern Nations, he belonged to his mother's clan and not to his father's. So it was her Killer Whale that glinted from the copper ring around his neck, her Killer Whale that glared out, black and fierce, from his wide-brimmed rainhat. The Killer Whale crest was tattooed on Yaloa's skin to identify him forever.

"Killer Whale!" his mother often exclaimed. "Like Killer Whale, Yaloa, you and I are of the sea."

But how could he be of the sea when he lived so far upriver? His mother's clansmen, and his, lived away downriver in a coastal village. There they were sea-hunters. And Yaloa, as heir to their head chief, was expected to become a superb hunter of seals and sea otters and bellowing, whiskered sea lions. Yet he had no chance to learn.

His mother was anxious about it. Her brother, the great head chief Hay-il, had not yet sent for Yaloa; and there were other, younger heirs who might lay claim to the title.

"Why doesn't your uncle send for you?" she demanded. "My sisters' sons will be great sea-hunters," she would remind her own son. For they, his rivals, lived in coastal villages close to that of their honored uncle, Chief Hay-il. "Every day they are out on the sea, learning its ways."

8

But how could he go out on the sea to learn its ways?

"Go out on the river!" she constantly commanded. "Become brilliantly skillful with the paddle!" Like most high-ranking women, she was ambitious for her son. And she knew that it took worth, as well as birth, to make a claim to a great name valid. If her son could not win sea power, then he never would be entrusted with the head chieftainship of a sea-hunting clan. "Go out on the river! Win salmon power!" For though they moved in and out of the rivers, the salmon were of the sea. "Hunt river otters!"

Yaloa went out on the river. Again and again and again and again, he went out on the river. Even when other Killer Whale boys in his village went off into the hills to learn the ways of the mountain goat, Yaloa went out on the river to hunt river otters. And he dared not look reluctant.

"What a noble must do," his mother kept reminding him, "he must do with grace and spirit."

"What a noble must do," he in turn reminded his four official, noble young companions, "he must do with grace and spirit." They had to go with him.

And because he outranked them, the four boys swallowed their complaints. They merely narrowed their eyes and clamped their mouths shut when other boys went off into the hills without them. Then they exchanged conspiratorial glances. "What a noble must do, he must do with grace and spirit," they

9

agreed, taking every opportunity to dump the prince into the river. Gracefully, of course, and with spirit.

Not unnaturally, Yaloa began to resent the river. He began to resent the river otters. He began to resent even the lovely, silver salmon that leaped up the waterfalls.

And they, no doubt sensing his resentment, eluded his spear and dip net. In a village of superb fishermen, the prince could not catch a salmon.

"You have no salmon power," his mother said with dismay. "No sea power at all!"

Yaloa began to cheer himself up by slipping away from his four attendants to try his luck at catching eagles. At those times, Yaloa was almost happy. For he had a very special feeling about eagles. They were so gloriously high and free!

No wonder eagle feathers made the best arrows for mountain-goat hunters, he always thought, watching them circle high above him. The swiftness and hunting skill of the great Chief of the Air lived even in his feathers. So those feathers gave speed and force to the hunter's arrow. And an eagle feather tied into a hunter's hair helped him to be what he must be, fleet as a flying bird.

Yaloa tied an eagle feather into his own hair hopefully. For who knew? If he never won sea power, he might yet have a chance to be a mountain-goat hunter. Of course, he always took the feather out before his sharp-eyed mother saw it. She must never know that he escaped from his duty on the river to go off catching eagles. That is, to go off to try catching eagles. For the prince seemed to have no eagle power either.

With his slave boy Lax doing most of the work, Yaloa had made a good eagle-catching pit and concealed it with branches. And whenever Lax was fishing for the bait, Yaloa dreamed of the great bird who would circle high above his trap, its eyes alert for the flash of his fish. For, like himself, the lordly eagle preferred to let others do his fishing for him.

Later, crouched in the pit, Yaloa always watched the circling with joyous envy. In spite of what people seemed to think, eagles, not salmon, were the great ones. A fish was merely the helpless victim of the lordly eagle. Yaloa felt a secret kinship with the eagle. In fact, he usually watched its dive toward his bait with such utter identification that he forgot to grab the bird's legs when the time came. He lost all his eagles that way and all his bait. He also lost the admiration of his slave boy, who had been waiting nearby with his club ready.

So, Yaloa had never caught an eagle. But his slave's sharp eyes found so many eagle feathers that the prince always had plenty for his hair and his arrows and for making his four companions think that he was good at catching eagles. In fact, word of his skill went around the village.

And the word reached his mother.

"Why don't you try catching red flickers?" she suggested. And Yaloa knew why. Flicker feathers could help a sea-hunter the way eagle feathers could help a landsman. A sea-hunter could slip flicker feathers reverently into the ocean on the blade of his paddle as a gift to the Ocean People. For those spirits of the deep must be kept friendly.

"Fwaw!" he burst out to Lax when his mother had gone. He would never win sea power. And his mother ought to know that. Wasn't she always reminding him that a sea hunter must be out on the sea from his earliest childhood to learn its ways? Was it his fault that he wasn't? His uncle didn't want him.

He tried harder to catch an eagle.

"Why don't you try catching flickers?" his mother demanded.

This time he had his answer ready.

"In a roundabout way, eagle feathers help a sea-hunter," he blustered to her. And it was true. For no spearpoint, no harpoon barb was better than one made from the hard, black tip of a mountain-goat horn. "The sure leap of the goat lives on in its horn to help the sea-hunter," he reminded his mother.

She did not smile fondly at his answer. She merely hid the shame in her eyes. And Yaloa knew what she was thinking. She had had high hopes for him. And now it was being rumored that her younger sister's sons—heirs after Yaloa—were the likelier successors to her brother, Chief Hay-il. It was being rumored that they were living already in his Killer Whale House. Certainly they were being accustomed to the ways of the seals and the sea otters, while the true heir stayed upriver with the mountain goats.

"He'll soon be sending for you," his mother said, half in hope and half in warning. "Or even coming for you!"

But Hay-il did not come to see his heir, much less to take him back to the proper village to train him for the chiefhood. He did not even send the looked-for invitation. And Yaloa's four friends showed less and less respect for their royal comrade. Only his slave boy stayed constant, having no choice.

"Perhaps rumors have reached your uncle's ears," his mother chided him anxiously whenever she caught him mooning over eagle feathers or watching the best arrow-makers. Rumors that he was not seeking sea power, she meant. Rumors that he was not training diligently to please the Great Salmon Spirit.

"Stop feeding the rumors!" she ordered. Then she redoubled her own hopeful preparations for her brother's arrival, or for his messengers' arrival. She set aside the best of the remaining smoked fish. She stored up the best of the remaining berry cakes for Chief Hay-il or his noble envoys. And she eagerly watched the river for the first silver glint of the beautiful new spring salmon.

Just in case the awesome uncle did arrive, Yaloa made one wild attempt to win salmon power. And, as though the fish-catching skill in his eagle hair feathers and the sure leap in his mountain goat-horn spear-tip joined forces to help him, he speared a big salmon —an enormous spring salmon! The first of the run up the river. Yanked into the river by its strength, the prince got an unplanned lesson in swimming. But he hung on, mainly because he was afraid to let go in the icy, rushing water.

His four companions leaped eagerly in to help him land the salmon, while his slave boy tripped over the fish club in sheer surprise and excitement.

His mother was jubilant.

"The very Chief of all the Salmon!" she whispered in awe. "You have salmon power, Yaloa. Oh, you have salmon power! And this salmon must be kept as proof of the word that will go racing down the river to your uncle's ears. Perhaps he was waiting for a great sign." New hope shone in her dark eyes. Her son was proving himself worthy of the chieftainship. Surely, now Hay-il would send for Yaloa to install him in his rightful place in Killer Whale House. Now dances would be danced and gifts would be given in her son's honor at a great potlatch.

She smoked the Chief of all the Salmon with reverent care while the villagers chanted to honor the salmon's spirit.

Yaloa watched, a little stunned by the whole affair.

"Return the bones to the river, Yaloa!" his mother commanded, just as she was called away.

More than a little embarrassed by his sudden prestige, Yaloa relayed the job to Lax, his slave boy. He simply picked up a few scattered bones and bits and chucked them carelessly into the flowing water. Nobody in the village bothered much about the ancient custom of returning the bones with grace and ceremony.

Later, Yaloa watched as his mother folded the Chief of all the Salmon carefully away in a food box that was carved with the proudest of the Killer Whale totems. She put the precious box inside another box and yet another. And no one dared to touch it.

Summer passed, without any word from Hay-il. And still no one dared to touch the salmon.

Even when winter came, and then when winter

stretched on into a cold, hungry time, no one dared to touch the salmon. The proof of Yaloa's salmon power was sacred in Eagle House. It must be there to back the rumors that obviously had been slower than expected in spreading downriver to his uncle's ears.

By and by, the ice melted and the hungry time was over. And then there was no need to touch the salmon.

"But if I have salmon power, why must we hang on to this one salmon?" Yaloa demanded of his slave boy.

"Because you will never catch another big one," Lax suggested.

It was true. The prince couldn't even catch a small one. And it was all very humiliating. Yet the Chief of all the Salmon stayed folded in its nest of boxes, waiting for the great chief who did not seem eager to claim his true heir.

Pride kept Yaloa's mother from taking her son to her brother's house uninvited.

And humiliation kept Yaloa escaping more and more often from his none-too-respectful comrades. He had his slave boy and his eagles and his growing skill at making arrows. But it was a bad year for Yaloa.

It was a bad year for everybody. The salmon were strangely scarce.

Shamans put on their bear-claw crowns and their clattering, deer-hoof-fringed dancing aprons. They danced and shook their medicine rattles. And the anxious, watching people became more careful than they had been about the old salmon taboos: They drank reviving fresh water immediately after eating salmon; they returned the bits and bones carefully to the river. And they chanted at the riverbank, "You are all chiefs!" to entice the salmon and please the Great Salmon Spirit.

Yet the salmon did not come into the river in their usual plenty.

Scouts reported scanty tribes of fish moving in from the sea, with seals following them in to deplete what there was. Otters waited to snatch their share, and bears ranged hungrily along the banks of the streams. Gulls screamed and fought and stole from the fishermen below the hungry, circling eagles.

Yaloa's eyes still delighted in the eagle's flight. But he felt more and more guilty about making Lax fish for eagle bait. Still he had to catch an eagle, he told himself. He had to make more eagle-feathered arrows. Since there was a desperate shortage of salmon, the village was going to need extra meat.

But when the hunting time came, goats were strangely scarce in the mountains.

Shamans put on their bear-claw crowns again, and their clattering, deer-hoof-fringed aprons. They danced even more frantically and shook their medicine rattles. Yet the mountains stayed strangely empty, like the rivers.

"The spirits are offended," people muttered to one another. And there was alarm in their eyes and voices.

But even when the world seemed locked in snow and ice, and when the Spirit of Hunger stalked the land, her bones rattling in her ghost skin and her hag hair streaming out on the fierce gales, still no one dared to touch the stored Chief of all the Salmon, the proof of Yaloa's power.

He caught angry glances directed at him. He heard angry mutters.

"It is taboo to store salmon a second winter," people said, louder and louder in the prince's hearing. "The spirits of the salmon are offended. And all the animal spirits."

"All the animal spirits are indeed offended," Yaloa's mother retorted whenever the words reached her ears. "I wonder that salmon ever come near your nets. I wonder that mountain goats ever come into your hunting grounds. All of you carelessly scatter the bones and bits about."

It was taboo to scatter bones about. According to the old tribal laws, bones were to be carefully burned or carefully returned to the water so that animal spirits could use them again. Everybody knew that. But the tribe had grown careless through years of plenty. And now, when the spirits were obviously offended, people wanted to blame one another to make themselves feel less guilty.

Most of all, though, they wanted to blame Yaloa.

It was his salmon, they all agreed. It was his salmon, stored for a second winter, that was bringing the wrath of the animal spirits down on everybody.

Actually, they knew it was his mother who had stored the salmon. But she was a very great lady with a sea-otter robe and glistening abalone-shell earrings and a magnificently tall Killer Whale hat. She was the wife of their own beloved chief. So it was safer to blame a mere boy—especially a boy who did not even belong in the village. Chief Hay-il should have sent for his useless nephew long ago.

Sensitive to their glances and mutterings, Yaloa stayed away from everybody, everybody except Lax. Though Lax sniveled.

Not being a noble like Yaloa, or even a proper, long-haired member of some clan, Lax could snivel about his empty belly. He could throw back his shorn head and howl when he was hungry.

A prince like Yaloa could only suffer in noble silence.

"An aristocrat does what is to be done with grace and spirit," his mother kept reminding him. A prince gracefully refused to eat until he was assured of food for everybody. And in times of famine, he contented himself with chewing on a bit of mountain-goat fat to stave off actual starvation. For greed and gluttony were the most ignoble of all traits. Only a slave boy dared bellow about his belly.

Yaloa was gracefully chewing on the very last bit

19

of fat, and Lax was really bellowing, on the day the rest of Eagle House went off to gather a certain bark to eat; for all the good food was gone.

"You must stay to guard the fire, Yaloa," his mother had said in a voice clear enough for all to hear. But he had known why she was leaving him. The people didn't want to take a spirit-offending person with them into the forest. They had troubles enough already.

When they had gone, he concentrated on the beautiful arrow he was feathering. And he pressed his lips tightly together. Only his belly groaned. His belly and his slave boy.

"I'm starving," Lax wailed, over and over and over again. "My bones are knocking together inside my skin."

"Be quiet!" Yaloa ordered.

But even Lax was no longer respectful to the Killer Whale prince. "I'm too hungry to be quiet," he protested.

Yaloa's hands were on the eagle feathers. But his mind kept darting off to the first robin. It would come, one of these days. And it would sing that the ice was melting in the Nass River to the north of them; that the small, silver oolachan fish were rushing into all their special rivers. His mouth watered at the thought of the rich, delicious, small fish that always ushered in the time of plenty. And when he mentioned it to Lax, the slave boy really wailed.

By the end of the day, Yaloa was at his wits' end. "If you'll shut up, I'll find you something to eat," he said finally, in desperation.

Lax's whimpering was cut off as suddenly and as completely as the flight of a stunned bird. He fixed hopeful eyes on his master.

Now Yaloa had to feed him. He had given a prince's promise. But what was there to eat? Hopeful of even a slug or a spider, his glance ranged wildly about the big house, past the carved posts, the sleeping platforms, and the Eagle-painted screens until it chanced on the nest of boxes. His mother's most treasured food boxes.

"The Chief of all the Salmon," he whispered. Then held his breath.

Lax was silent with surprise for several seconds. Then, "But . . . but . . . but . . . but . . ." he protested.

"But nothing!" Yaloa snapped. And he rushed angrily at the awesome boxes. The proof of his salmon power. "Fwaw!" he said, almost in tears. He lifted the first lid. "FWAW!" he thundered again to bolster his failing courage. He raised the second lid, revealing the smallest box, where the smoked fish was waiting —the fish that foolishly was being treasured to prove that he was what he was not. To impress an uncle who didn't want him. Defiantly he raised the third lid.

The smell of smoked salmon rushed into his nostrils, and into Lax's. And though the fish was a little moldy, the smell made Yaloa weak with longing.

Lax was still, stunned and silent. But now his tongue was licking at his lips. His eyes were devouring the salmon.

"It's mine. I caught it," Yaloa said, loudly, to convince himself. Then, with shaking hands, he unfolded the fish. He broke a piece off. He shoved it at his slave boy. Then, trembling, he closed the three lids.

He was still standing there, shocked at his own deed, when the people came in. He had not even licked his fingers. In fact, he was staring at his hands in horror when his mother strode in.

She sniffed. Lifted one of the offending hands. Then threw it from her as she might have thrown off a devilfish.

"You?" she gasped, in sheer disbelief.

She thought he had eaten the salmon, when the people were starving. And he was too shocked to answer.

Angry as fire, she opened the lids. And the people leaned toward the ravishing smell of the salmon.

The great lady moved her hand in regal invitation. "I have no wish to keep the proof of what my son is," she said. And her voice was as cold and as hard as the ice in a glacier.

The words came like a spear. Yaloa staggered. And then, like a wounded animal, he rushed away into the bush. Unmindful of the gale that whipped at his scanty clothing or of the branches that tore at his flesh, he stumbled blindly along until he came to a spot where the river roared out of a rocky canyon to race, dark and swift, down to the sea. He stood on the riverbank, unmindful of anything but the shame of his mother's words.

Now the word *would* spread along the river. The whole world would whisper that Yaloa was not only a useless nephew whom no uncle would want, but was also a greedy glutton, a noble who would sneak food for himself while the tribe was starving. He would never live this deed down. It would cling to him forever, like the Killer Whale tattoo they would say he had dishonored.

Yaloa swayed toward the dark, racing river. Sunk in the misery of public shame, he scarcely heard the voices on the river, calling his name. He scarcely saw the big canoe that seemed to gather every bit of the failing light until it shone like a silver salmon. He barely noticed the arms that caught him.

Then he was lying in the big canoe, silent, with four silent men. No one was paddling. Yet the strange craft was slipping downriver as adept as a salmon. And its sides were lifting and coming together, lifting and coming together until they closed over his head.

By and by, he sensed the downward tilt of the salmon canoe as it rushed into the deep, deep sea, out toward the horizon.

Meanwhile, in Eagle House, few noticed the prince's escape. Most eyes, including Lax's, were greedily fixed on the salmon.

The Eagle Chief motioned his portion away from him, while his eyes kept searching the dark corners for his son. Yaloa could not stay out long in that bitter night without his fur robe, his father knew. The boy must slip back in.

The chief turned alertly at Lax's sudden, loud wail.

Lax had finally missed his master. And he had realized what had happened. Worse still, he had realized what could happen. A slave could be killed for failing to stay with his master. So he howled.

"Be quiet!" the Eagle Chief ordered.

Lax stopped. And the whole house hushed itself.

"Lax, where is your master?"

"Gone. He ran away." Lax renewed his howling, as much for his own fate as for his master's. Then he stopped once again. Since life had not allowed him to be noble, it had trained him to be cunning. And now, he sensed, he had better turn people's thoughts away from his wretched self to his wretched master. "The prince didn't eat," he screeched, as though with no other aim than to defend his master's honor. "He fed me. He didn't even lick his fingers."

The Eagle Chief turned toward his startled lady. "You heard Lax," he said. "He did not even lick his fingers." Then he turned to the watching people. "You heard. The prince fed only his starving slave

24

boy. From his own fish. From the salmon he caught. Now, we will find my son!"

Men rushed to light their pitchwood torches.

Women hurried to put their wraps back on.

"He was a great catcher of eagles," they remembered, and their tones suggested that it was a very fine thing to catch eagles.

"A skilled arrow-maker!" they proclaimed.

"And a kind master," they added, indicating the slave boy who was once again howling.

They found Yaloa's tracks in the snow and followed them to the riverbank.

There the tracks ended.

"My son is dead," the Eagle Chief said, out of the awful silence.

A low singing started, and slowly swelled into a wild lament for the lost, wronged prince of the Killer Whales. For they could at least give him a good name in the Land of Souls, and so make themselves feel less guilty about the bad name they had given him in the Land of Men.

"My son is dead," his mother said. And her voice was shattered, like a great tree that had been struck by lightning.

Only one old, old shaman was still and silent, as though straining to hear something beyond the others' hearing.

Wakened by a gentle hand on his shoulder, Yaloa

opened his eyes.

It was a strange, silvery day.

He sat up in the strange canoe. "Where am I?" he whispered.

But he did not need to ask. The carvings on the nearby houses told him where he was, and the silver glints on the housefronts and totem poles. He was at the fabled village of the Salmon People, in the supernatural world beyond the horizon.

He controlled his trembling. If he was in the supernatural world, then he must have drowned back there in the river.

Or—

He remembered the arms that had caught him. He had been carried off like one of the princes in the tribe's ancient stories.

But why? Why had he been brought here, to the supernatural village where, people said, the salmon began their mysterious journey to the rivers.

He looked anxiously at the village that edged the beach. There was not one familiar crest, not one reassuring Eagle or Killer Whale, not one Wolf or Bear or Raven. Only strange starfish and kelp and octopus designs were carved on the ends of the housebeams. And every housefront was painted with a salmon emblem. Every crestpole was topped by a salmon.

There were people moving about among the houses. And Yaloa caught his breath. They were the

salmon in human form. It was the human form they used until it was time for them to make their mysterious return to the rivers. The men who had brought him here were actually salmon.

But why had they brought him?

One possible reason made him swallow hard. The salmon had honored him—once—with salmon power. They had let him catch the very Chief of all the Salmon. And what had he done to honor them in return? Yaloa flushed as he remembered how he just stood there while the rest of the villagers had chanted the proper welcome. He flushed even more as he remembered how carelessly he had told Lax to chuck the bones and bits into the river. The people had been right. It was he who had really offended the animal spirits. And now they had him completely in their power.

Controlling himself as a prince must, he followed his four boatmen to the very large house in the center of the village, the house most magnificently carved. The other houses carried only Spring Salmon totems, but this large central house was beautifully decorated with the forms of all kinds of salmon: Spring, Sockeye, Coho, Humpback, Keta. . . .

"The Chief of all the Salmon," he thought, with increasing alarm. And as he ducked in through the opening in the housepole, he could not help remembering the tale of a people who had once invited an enemy into their chief's house only to lop off his head as he ducked in.

But nothing happened.

Blinking to see in the dim light of the immense, windowless house, he peered anxiously about. But all he could really see was the chief's robe in the rear, beyond the fire. Silver as a salmon, it seemed dazzling in the smoky gloom of the great cedar house.

As he approached, and looked more closely, he saw that the robe was pulled about a wasted, reclining figure.

"The Chief of all the Salmon People has been very sick for nearly two years," an old woman whispered, touching Yaloa.

"Sick?" Who had made him sick? the boy wondered with a start. When someone was sick, there was always a reason, and often the reason was the carelessness of some other person. He did wish he wouldn't keep thinking about the great fish that he had not bothered to honor.

The old woman slipped away without saying another word. And the chief was too weak to do more than courteously express the welcome of the Salmon People.

Welcome? Why was he welcome? As a slave to serve them? Well, he was not a slave. So at least he would not mention his empty belly, though the chief's welcome did not appear to include the usual offer of food.

Supernatural people did not need to eat, he remembered. So he couldn't have been drowned and become supernatural himself. He was hungry as a gull. Hungry as a raven. But he couldn't mention it, as Lax could have.

For the first time, Yaloa thought of his slave boy with consternation. A slave could be killed for failing to stay with his master. He should have grabbed Lax by the scruff of his neck and yanked him into the bushes.

When he felt he could, Yaloa slipped out of Salmon House to look around. And soon happy shouts drew him toward a sandhill in back of the houses, where the children of the village were playing. He watched their games with interest. Every darting movement of the players, every great leap reminded him of a salmon. "Of course!" he murmured. "Those children are salmon."

He felt a hand touch him, as it had touched him before in the chief's house. And again it was the old woman.

"Sometime when you are hungry," she said, "take a club and club one of those children playing on the sandhill."

"One of those children?" He was really shocked.

"You would club a salmon," she pointed out reasonably.

"Yes, but. . . ."

The prince stayed hungry a long, long time. By the time he finally did pick up a club, he was almost too weak to lift it. And he was too faint to do more than tap one of the smallest children.

Instantly, to his utter astonishment, the child was gone, and a beautiful little spring salmon was lying at his feet, wriggling. And none of the other children appeared to pay any attention.

Wild to snatch up the fish, yet afraid to touch it, Yaloa stood looking at it.

He felt the old woman's hand. Then he heard her voice. "Make a fire and roast it. And when you have eaten it and taken the reviving drink of fresh water, gather up all the bones and bits and put them into the water."

Yaloa snatched up the fish, ran to a secluded place beyond the sandhill, lit a fire, and roasted the lovely little salmon.

When he had eaten every last bit of its flesh, he sat feeling wonderfully contented. Then he remembered what he must do. So he went to the brook to drink fresh water. Then he gathered up the bones and bits and put them into the water.

By and by, when the light was failing, he went back into Salmon House.

A small child was crying.

When Yaloa's eyes became accustomed to the smoky gloom of the great cedar house, he caught his breath. For the small child who was crying was the very child he had clubbed when he had been too desperately hungry to stay hungry any longer. The very

31

child! Only now it was shrieking with pain and holding its hands over one eye. "My eye is sore. O, my eye is sore," it was screeching. And it seemed to shrink away from the beckonings of the strangely silent people who seemed always to be hovering on the edge of lively tribal life.

The old woman touched Yaloa to get his attention. "Go quickly!" she whispered. "Go and search your roasting pit!"

Not quite understanding, Yaloa rushed out. He raced to the spot where he had roasted his little spring salmon. And he searched carefully all around it.

"An eye!" he said, pouncing on the one thing he had missed when gathering up the bones and bits. He darted over to the brook and put the eye into the water.

Straining to hear as he hurried back to Salmon House, he heard only the sounds of talk and laughter. And when he ducked in through the hole, he saw the very child jumping up and down for joy. Both eyes were shining.

Yaloa swallowed. He wet his dry lips. It was a very strange happening. And when the chief motioned to him, he went to the rear as gracefully as he could, though he felt a little nervous.

The chief merely smiled wanly at him.

"You . . . you look a little better tonight, Chief of all the Salmon People," he ventured to say, out of an unnerving silence.

"I am a little better now, thanks to you," the chief answered. Then smiling weakly, he waved his guest from him.

"Thanks to me?" Yaloa mumbled as he moved away from the weary old man.

"You opened the box," the old woman mumbled back, from somewhere behind him.

"Opened the box?" Understanding began to dawn on him. But did they know what he had done about the bones and bits of the Chief of all the Salmon? Perhaps they didn't know that it was he who had carelessly left it to Lax to look after the bones and bits that day. Perhaps they didn't know that his opening of the box had had nothing of care in it, either, unless you counted care for his own ears, which had been weary of Lax's wailing.

The next day the Chief of all the Salmon People sent his scouts to the rivers of the real world to see if the cottonwood leaves had arrived yet.

"The cottonwood leaves," Yaloa whispered to himself. And his voice was full of yearning. If only he could smell the honeyed fragrance that drifted along the river when the sticky buds opened in the springtime! If only he could see the golden green of the new leaves lighting the riverbank against the deep blues and greens of the mountains! If only he could taste one of the spring salmon that arrived with the new leaves!

He felt such a longing for the taste of spring

salmon that he raced to the sandhill in back of the houses and clubbed another small child, a fatter one this time.

As before, the child instantly vanished. As before, a tiny spring salmon lay at his feet, wriggling. A fatter one this time.

"When you have eaten it," the now familiar old voice said, "and when you have taken the reviving drink of water, gather up all the bones and bits and put them into the water!"

This time Yaloa was more careful. He was sure he had gathered all the bones and bits up before he went back to Salmon House. But even before he reached it, he heard the screeching.

Protesting his innocence to himself, he ducked in through the opening in the housepole. And sure enough, there was the very child—the fatter one—holding both hands over its ribcage, screeching, "My rib is sore. O, my rib is sore!"

Before the old woman had a chance to touch Yaloa or speak to him, he darted out of the house and sprinted back to his roasting pit beyond the sandhill. He searched a long time before he found one tiny fish rib under a cedar chip. Then he swooped it up and dropped it into the water.

Sure enough, when he got back to Salmon House, the fat child was happily playing.

He caught a look of pain on the chief's face; but it was gone in an instant. And the Chief of all the

Salmon People was smiling at him.

"I wish. . . ." Yaloa closed his mouth over the wish that he could go back to his father's village and search for certain other bones. But it was too late now. He would never go back.

He waited eagerly for word of his native river.

But the scouts returned empty-handed. "There were no leaves to bring yet," they reported. "Still, the buds are swelling into honeyed fragrance."

Such a wave of longing for that honeyed fragrance swept over Yaloa that he closed his eyes.

"You, too, would like to return to the river," a gentle voice remarked.

Yaloa swung around to see Alulal, the chief's granddaughter, a slim, stately girl Yaloa had often seen walking about with her four maidens. She fairly glistened in her silvered blue-green robe and her blue-green abalone-shell ornaments.

"One day I will go to our river—yours and mine," she went on. And her voice reminded the prince of a crystal stream, dancing down the mountain.

"I'll go with you," he burst out, before he remembered that he would never go.

Her pearly earrings gleamed, iridescent blue-green, with the gentle shake of her head. And the sadness in the glance she swept over him startled Yaloa. A sudden, wild yearning raced through the prince. But he knew that his yearning for Alulal was as hopeless as his yearning for the scents of spring-

35

time along his native river.

Swept along by a new despair, he rushed out to the beach and threw himself into the sea.

And an amazing thing happened. As though born to the sea, he gloried in its buoyant waters. He found himself diving and twisting and darting like a minnow. Why had he so resisted his heritage of the sea? he wondered.

From then on, he could not resist the sea. Morning, noon, and night he was out in its waters.

"You will be turning into a salmon," Alulal told him. And Yaloa fancied that he caught a hope in her gentle voice.

The scouts were sent out again. And this time they came back with cottonwood leaves.

Yaloa feasted his eyes on the glistening golden-green of the new leaves. He closed his eyes to drink deeply of their fragrance.

Now the Chief of all the Salmon People put on a red-and-silver robe, as though dressing up for a potlatch. He put on a sea-green headdress circled with sea-lion bristles and gleaming with blue-green discs of iridescent abalone shell. He summoned all the people of the tribe into Salmon House. And they came in black-spangled silver and brown-spangled silver robes, in blue-green and red-and-silver dancing blankets, as though it were, indeed, a potlatch.

But where were the canoeloads of guests? Where were the gifts piled ready for the giving? Where were the mountains of food, ready for the feasting?

Men danced and scattered eagle down while others drummed on hollow cedar. And women chanted.

Then, speaking through the magnificent nobleman who held his Talking Stick, the wasted old chief addressed the people:

"Great Tribe!" he said. "The canoes are coming!"

So there were canoes coming! It *was* a potlatch! Yaloa slipped out eagerly to join in the tribe's welcome of its visitors.

A fleet of strange, silvery canoes seemed to draw themselves up along the beach. But they were empty. No one was coming to the potlatch. Yet the whole tribe danced toward the high-prowed canoes, chanting, while drummers drummed and shamans shook their rattles and chiefs scattered eagle down in the age-old pledge of peace.

"Of course," Yaloa muttered, finally understanding. "The return to the rivers." This was the ceremonial sendoff, not a welcome. It was time for the salmon's mysterious return to the rivers.

"The river!" All Yaloa's yearning for home was in his eyes as he watched the preparations for departure. Strong old men and women held the canoes out in the water while strong young men and women climbed aboard.

He felt a hand touch him.

"Go with them," the old woman said.

"But. . . ." The chance to go startled him.

"But come back," Alulal whispered, handing him a small rounded quartz pebble. "The Stone of Safety," she explained. "A gift from grandfather. While you keep this in your mouth, Yaloa, danger cannot touch you, nor death."

"Death?" The word jolted him. His wild urge to go was engulfed in a wild urge to not go. Nothing but shame awaited him in the village. He felt Alulal's eyes on him—wondering if he was afraid to make the mysterious journey? Obviously, nothing but shame awaited him here if he didn't go. His shoulders slumped in despair.

But a noble must do what had to be done with grace and spirit. So Yaloa squared his shoulders. He made a gesture of respectful gratitude toward Alulal and put the stone in his mouth. Then he walked lightly toward one of the strange canoes.

As he neared the canoe, he was pushed and jostled by a group of people—the sad-looking people who always huddled in the corners, silently haunting the edge of lively tribal life. Now that their robes were flung back, Yaloa saw that they were the halt and the lame; they were the people who had been injured.

And they were desperate to go off with the others. But the strong old men and women held them back. The strong young men and women threw them out of the canoes. Only beautiful people in their prime could go off to the rivers of the real world.

Off to the rivers of the real world!

Yaloa's heart was hammering as the strange canoes slid silently out to sea. And his tongue was pressed hard against the Stone of Safety.

First they came to an island where there was another town with salmon-carved houses. Here all the silver decoration was blue-tinged, and there were brilliant splashes of red on the housefronts and totem crestpoles. It was the supernatural village of the Sockeye Salmon People. And some of them put out in canoes to speak to the travelers.

"How is it in the rivers?" they called when they were close enough.

In answer, the travelers' canoe chiefs waved their little sprigs of cottonwood leaves.

"We will follow at the right time," the villagers promised, naming their rivers and cheering the travelers on their way.

Next, they came to the village of the Humpback Salmon People. Again, canoes put off and the people called out, "We will follow you as soon as the Steelhead People have passed on their way home from the rivers." They named their rivers and cheered the travelers on their way.

At the next village of salmon-carved houses, the Coho Salmon People called out, "We will wait until the golden leaves have fallen."

And so it went, with all the different tribes of Salmon People agreeing to move out to various rivers at various times.

Then, when all had been well arranged, the Spring Salmon People's canoes slipped swiftly toward the horizon.

Yaloa could see it ahead of them, rising like a blue wall. Beyond it, he knew, was the real world.

The chief of his canoe spoke now. "We will wait at the horizon until it has lifted four times. Then we will all slip through together."

Yaloa swallowed. He had heard that the belt of light on the horizon hid a strange opening and closing that allowed people to pass between the real world and the supernatural. He also had heard of a supernatural bird of prey that hovered near the opening to snatch up the unwary. His teeth clenched shut and his tongue pressed hard against the magical Stone of Safety.

As they approached the blue wall, the canoes moved into line, their sides almost touching one another.

A section of the wall lifted, then closed again so quickly that Yaloa caught his breath. How would they ever slip through fast enough? He watched it a second time, and a third time, and a fourth time.

How would they ever slip through fast enough? When the wall started to lift again, he held his breath. Then lost it in the instant dart of the canoe, through, into the real world. He glanced back. The horizon was closed. He was back in the real world. But he was there alone.

For as the strange canoes slipped through the horizon, all the Spring Salmon People dived into the water and disappeared into the great swells of the Pacific Ocean.

Alone in the canoe, Yaloa watched the rolling and leaping of the living silver fish all around him. He sensed their wild ecstasy. Fascinated, he leaned toward the water, scarcely aware of a whirring blackness above him.

Then he was in the sea. In the very center of a swift, shining tribe of spring salmon. And the wild ecstasy thrilled through his body, too. He found delight in the flow of cool, green water along his strangely smooth sides and in the power of his own strange thrust through the ocean. He marveled at the instant response of his strange, new body to the currents of the ocean, joining the instant response of the long, streamlined, shadowy silver-green bodies around him. They all moved as one, darting, diving, rising to the surface, and always racing into the current. They hurled their strength against the strength of the sea, and gloried in their own power.

He could not have turned into a salmon! Yaloa

knew that he must be dreaming. But how could he be dreaming in such cold, deep, green water? He felt wildly awake.

Still moving as one, the tribe of spring salmon slashed through tribes of needlefish and herring; and the needlefish and herring scattered in a million flashes of living silver.

Supernaturally freed from hunger, the salmon moved through masses of luminously pink shrimps, through drifts of opalescent squid. And the cold, green water flowed past the swift, streamlined bodies in silence.

Then Yaloa sensed a darkening in his world. He felt panic in the swift scatter of his own tribe. And he dived for the black depths. He huddled with others in the murky darkness until the killer whales had gone and the salmon tribe had re-formed around him. And when they moved on, he pressed his mouth hard around the tiny Stone of Safety. Nothing could harm him while he held it in his mouth. Nothing! No killer whale. No shark. No sea lion could tear his bright flesh.

They traveled on, and on.

Then he began to sense a mounting excitement in the salmon around him. He sensed a freshening in the water. They were nearing a river. When they rolled and leaped on the surface, he heard the gulls; he saw the gathering of the hungry, dark seals.

He pressed the pebble harder and harder as the

tribe of spring salmon rested for several days in a shallow before heading into the racing current of the river. They did not feed. After living in the supernatural world, hunger was no longer in them. But it was everywhere around them. The dark, wet heads of seals moved hungrily through the water. The hungry gulls screamed. Hungry ospreys watched. Hungry eagles circled. Everywhere, on all sides, was hunger. And along the river, hungry land otters would be waiting, and hungry bears, and many, many hungry people.

When the salmon moved into the river, their spirited splashings churned the water white from shore to shore. And their wild, graceful leaps kept the white surface flashing. It was as if they were dancing and scattering eagle down to welcome the eager hordes who came hungrily to the river.

Lost in awe, Yaloa felt as far as ever from understanding the ancient mystery of the salmon. Why did they return so joyously to the river when there was only death waiting?

They must know that death was waiting for them.

But who knew what was waiting for the Killer Whale prince?

Reluctance grew in him with every thrust up the cold, gray, racing river.

Far upriver, Yaloa's mother was watching for the salmon run almost with bated breath. For a shaman

had had a vision. He had seen her son in the supernatural village of the Salmon People. And now the
salmon were coming.

The tribe had come to its fishing station near the
canyon. Dip nets had been readied. And now everyone waited. Everyone watched the river. Everyone
chanted.

"You are all chiefs," they chanted to entice the
salmon. "You are all chiefs," they chanted to please
the Great Salmon Spirit.

The shaman who had had the vision wore his
crown of grizzly bear claws as he stood on a special
platform with his long-poled dip net. He wore his
dancing apron. And he scattered eagle down on the
water.

Yaloa's mother stood near him. Her face was darkened, in mourning for her son. But her eyes were
bright with a strange, feverish hope as she watched
the shaman's dip net. She did not know what she expected. Yet she watched the dip net intently. Perhaps
there would be some sign.

She watched and watched and watched the shaman's dip net. And she saw a beautiful young spring
salmon leap into it.

"The Springs are arriving!" people shouted in
wild glee. But there was something they must do before they harvested the salmon. They must win back
the favor of the Great Salmon Spirit.

Yaloa's mother put on her sea-otter robe and her

most magnificent Killer Whale hat for the ceremonial welcome to the first spring salmon. Her eyes were anxious. If the Salmon People were holding her son in their supernatural village, then the greatest deference must be shown to the salmon's spirit. Nothing must be done to offend the salmon.

She watched as the beautiful young spring salmon was ceremoniously placed on a shredded-cedar mat on a handsomely carved cedar plank. She saw the sharp, mussel-shell knife cut deferentially into the silver skin. And she caught a glimpse of copper.

"My son's neck ring!" she gasped.

"The prince?" people muttered, falling back in awe. Could such a thing really happen?

"My son's neck ring!" she murmured again. Her son had become a salmon?

The shaman's rattle sounded. His deer-hoof fringe clattered. He was dancing a strange dance around the beautiful young spring salmon.

Now the people knew what to do. Remembering the old, old tales of the supernatural, they knew what to do. Reverently they carried the silver body to Eagle House. Reverently they placed it on the roof, where the reviving rains would wash away the supernatural and bring the human back to them.

The prince's four official companions kept watch at Eagle House while the rest of the tribe went back to its fishing. And Lax hovered nervously around the house, afraid to stay, yet terrified of being caught away from his strangely altered master.

As if eager to wash away the supernatural, the rain came in torrents. For four days, it pelted on the glistening young salmon.

Near the end of the fourth day, the four young guards fell into a deep, trance-like sleep. And they slept until morning.

Suddenly, their eyes flew open on a strange, silvery dawn, a strangely hushed dawn. Even the ravens' raucous call was muted.

Then Yaloa stood before them, taller than they had remembered, and with an odd brightness on his skin.

"But . . . but . . . but . . . but. . . ." Lax started whimpering, just to relieve his feelings.

"Be quiet!" Yaloa commanded his sniveling slave boy. "Tell my father!" he said to his four startled comrades.

They fled to the fishing station.

Lax fled with them. Then reconsidered. A slave could be killed for failing to stay with his master.

The Eagle Chief summoned the tribe to Eagle House to hear the story of his son's adventures. And the listeners flushed with shame when they heard of the halt and the lame in the Salmon People's village. They hurried to obey their chief's command to search out all the old bones and bits and return them to the river.

Yaloa did not need to be commanded. His mind's

eye was on the wasted figure of the Chief of all the Salmon People, Alulal's grandfather. And not until all the bones and bits had been searched out and apologetically returned to the river did he turn his thoughts to his own fate. Even then, he kept seeing the great old chief bounding with renewed vigor. He kept seeing Alulal's delight. She would know what had happened, and she would think kindly of him.

Here, he knew, people eyed him with suspicion. They looked at him very strangely. Perhaps they believed he had been turned into a fish as punishment for his greed that day when he had opened the boxes.

They looked at him very strangely. But, he noticed, they were very, very careful not to offend him.

Because they were afraid of him? Because they believed he had the power now to turn them into fish, too? He wondered about that as his life became more and more lonely.

This time word did spread swiftly along the river. Envoys arrived from Chief Hay-il with the long awaited invitation to the potlatch where Yaloa would be installed in an honored place in Killer Whale House.

"At last!" his mother said. Her voice was jubilant and her eyes shone with pride. "Perhaps, now, you will become a famous shaman."

That was his thought, too, now that he had been touched by the supernatural. Perhaps he would become a feverish skeleton of a man with long, wild hair straggling out from under a crown of grizzly bear claws. Perhaps he would spend his life making frenzied dances and fearsome spirit journeys.

But perhaps he would not be that lucky. Every time Yaloa went near the river, he felt the pull of the racing water. And he had a terrible conviction that he was fated to be a fish.

So he kept away from the river. He went back to catching eagles. He hung eagle feathers in his hair. He watched high flight with pure envy. If only he were an eagle! If only he could even catch an eagle!

Now his mother approved of catching eagles. It could produce great bags of eagle down. "This must be the greatest of all potlatches!" she told Yaloa. "Eagle down must float over the dancers like a glorious fall of snow!"

Eagle down. Yaloa's shoulders sagged. Lax might find fallen feathers, but he'd never find eagle down. Now he had to catch eagles.

Worst of all, he must catch eagles, yet he had to avoid the river where the bait was. In fact, he wanted to avoid fish altogether, because he was having wild dreams about being back in the ocean.

In his dreams, he felt the cool, green water flowing beautifully over his body. He felt the excitement of rolling and leaping on the surface. And he felt the security of others staying close around him. The dreams were lovely. But he worried about them.

49

He was standing alone one day, scowling at the mountains, when he felt a hand touch him, as it had touched him in the Salmon People's village. Yet there was nobody near him.

Then he heard the voice, the very voice he had heard in the Salmon People's village.

"Sometime when you want to catch an eagle," the voice said, "just stand on poles laid across the eagle pit and touch your head lightly with your fish club."

"Touch my own head with the fish club?" Yaloa protested.

But there was no one around to answer.

It was startling advice, as startling as the advice about clubbing one of the playing children. But that advice had worked. So he decided to give this advice a try, too.

"Lax!" he commanded, and the slave boy came scurrying to his side.

"We're going to catch an eagle," the prince informed him.

"After we catch the bait," Lax pointed out.

"Now," his master told him.

"But . . . but . . . but . . . but. . . ." A slave had to obey.

When they got to the pit, Yaloa said, "Find two good strong poles to lay across it. I'll get extra branches." Later he said, "You crouch in the pit, Lax! And see that you catch those eagle legs when they break through the branches!"

50

"But an eagle won't come. There's no bait."

"Then you won't worry about the talons," Yaloa answered briskly, as though he had nothing but blithe thoughts in his head.

Actually, his thoughts kept him pressing so hard on the Stone of Safety that it made his mouth ache. Tap his own head with a club? But when Lax was crouched in the pit, he laid the poles across and concealed the trap well with branches. Then he stood on the poles, watching the sky.

An eagle flew into sight, far above. "Chief of the Air," he whispered reverently.

Suddenly, he squared his shoulders. What a noble must do, he must do with grace and spirit. Then he swallowed—without swallowing the pebble. With his tongue he pressed it hard against the roof of his mouth, while he lifted his fish club. He closed his eyes. And he was trembling as he tapped his head.

Then he knew that he was lying on the branches, wriggling, while the eagle dived at him.

An instant before it touched him, he was human again; he was helping the screeching slave boy. While Lax hung on, yelling, Yaloa was clubbing the eagle.

He had caught an eagle. He had finally caught an eagle.

"What happened?" Lax screeched as he burst up through the branches.

"I caught an eagle," Yaloa answered, as though it were something he did any old day.

"Yes, but. . . ."

Yaloa did not explain. He wanted to push the happening from his mind. He did not want to think about it. And he desperately hoped he wouldn't dream about it. "Look after the bird, Lax!" he commanded briskly. Then, controlling his trembling, he led the way to the village.

His mother accepted the eagle jubilantly, while his four friends paid their respects to the great bird's spirit with wide-eyed astonishment. They knew where the prince's eagle feathers had previously come from.

"Eagle down will float over the dancers like a glorious fall of snow," his mother cried, obviously expecting a steady stream of eagles from her talented eagle-catcher. "This will be the greatest of all potlatches," she predicted. "Hay-il will honor you by giving magnificent canoes in your name and great beaten coppers." She could see the splendor of the giving with her mind's eye. "He'll give sea-otter robes and Chilkat blankets in your name, and glistening abalone earrings and carved mountain goat-horn spoons and . . . why not?" Her eyes widened with an idea. "Why not give bags of eagle down that you have provided?"

Yaloa hid his alarm.

"The greater the gifts, the greater the honor for you," his mother went on. "For the gifts show the wealth of the giver and his generous spirit. They are a display of the talent and industry of his people." She also meant, he knew, that the gifts not only proved the giver's current importance on the coast, but they also insured his future importance. For the recipients' pride in their own position would make them give back with interest on future occasions, at future potlatches. "Why not give bags of eagle down, too?" she urged. "When you are such a skilled eagle-catcher."

Yaloa silenced the question he saw on Lax's lips with a quick hand.

"I will bring you more eagles, Mother."

The prince rushed away in desperation. He had made another foolish promise. And he would have to keep it. Why was he always doing something desperate to escape humiliation? The potlatch! he thought bitterly. Arranged in *his* honor. "What if I turn up as a fish?" he muttered fiercely.

"What did you say?" Lax asked him, wide eyed.

"I said what if I turn up with a fish."

"But you never catch a fish."

No, he never caught a fish. And he didn't have to now to catch an eagle. Yaloa shuddered.

Turning into a fish of all things! Turning into a wretched little hunk of bait when he wanted to be something lordly, like an eagle. There was no doubt about it in his mind now; the eagle was far superior to the salmon. So why did people keep chanting, "You are all chiefs"? Why did the salmon rush so joyously up the river? Why did they leap so proudly? When there was nothing but death waiting for them.

As the season went by, as he caught more and more eagles, he sometimes sweated with the fear of losing the Stone of Safety. What if all this struggle to gain glory made him end up as a dead fish? As bleeding bait. As the victim of a lordly eagle.

More and more, people were looking at him strangely, yet jumping to do his bidding. He suspected that more boys than Lax were peering out through branches each time he captured an eagle. He suspected that strange rumors were flying around the village and racing along the river.

"Only one more eagle," he told his mother one day.

"Only one more," his mother agreed, so quickly he wondered if she, too, had been hearing rumors.

Why had he committed himself to even one more eagle? he asked himself fiercely. To even one more

baiting of the eagle trap? It always

Well. He *had* committed himself
going to back down.

It was well into the fall by that tin
leaves were gold along the river. And
ing shaken out in the sun and the bre
for the greatest of all the winter potla
salmon were running in the river, Yaloa
he desperately avoided the pull of the
They were running up to spawn in
gravelly creek beds.

"Only once more," Yaloa muttered.

Yet, though he knew he could stop tur
fish to bait the eagle trap, he knew he cou
his dreaming. More and more vividly in h
he was streaking through the cold, deep gree
he was glorying in the power of his thrust
the sea, and in the flow of the water along his
streamlined body, and in the rolling and lea
did on the surface of the water.

One night, the dream was especially vivid,
woke up with such a longing for the cold, green
that he crept silently out of Eagle House and ma
way to one of the spawning creeks. He didn't k
why he was rushing to the spawning creek. Bu
was as strong with purpose as a tribe of sock
salmon.

The sun was up by the time he reached the cre
bed. It was making beautiful, shifting patterns of lig

d shade in the swift-running crystal waters racing
er the pale gravel. And it was lighting the brilliant
d sides of the spawning sockeye salmon.

The salmon had lost their fresh sea silver. Now
heir great, gleaming sides were as red as an autumn
maple or an osier leaf. It was the exact shade of red
he Chief of all the Salmon People had put on the day
his young men and women started their return to the
rivers. And the sockeyes' heads—Yaloa caught his
breath. Now their heads were the exact shade of sea
green the old chief's ceremonial headdress had been.

"It's their dressing-up for the potlach," the voice
said.

Yaloa glanced about him, startled. But there was
nobody near him.

"It's their dressing-up for the potlach," the voice
repeated, the familiar voice of the old woman who
had advised him.

"Potlatch?" he asked, blankly. Yet he remembered
how he himself had thought "potlatch!" at the dressing in the Salmon People's village and at the entry
into fresh water. He remembered how it had been
when the salmon tribe had moved into the ravenous
river. Their spirited splashings had churned the water
white from shore to shore. Their wild, arched leaps
had kept the white surface flashing between the
stretches of dark timber that stood tall and straight
against the blue, snow-capped mountains. And it had
seemed to him then that the salmon were dancing and

scattering eagle down to welcome the eager hordes who came hungrily to the river.

"The greatest of all potlatches!" the old voice told him. "Everyone has come to the feast."

With his mind's eye, Yaloa saw the people with dip nets all along the river. He saw the bears ranging along the banks, the river otters diving, the gulls screaming overhead, under the circling eagles. Everyone had indeed come to the feast of the Salmon People. But the gifts?

"The greatest of all gifts, Yaloa."

He found his gaze focused on a pair of spawning salmon. The great female had dug her nest; and now she and her mate lay still, their brilliant sides touching. Suddenly, both seemed to shudder. Both were caught up in powerful vibrations. And the boy's quick eyes saw the stream of lovely, rosy, translucent eggs fall from the female, followed instantly by the white, fertilizing milt of the male.

The greatest of all gifts. "Of course!" The gift of life, of the life on which other life depended all along the river. People, otters, bears, gulls, eagles: all depended on the salmon.

Fascinated, he watched another salmon lay her rosy, translucent gift in the readied gravel; he watched the following white milt. The gifts of every salmon. Given with unfailing grace and spirit. Even death did not daunt them.

"You *are* all chiefs," he found himself saying. "You

are all chiefs." Every salmon gave the great gift magnificently.

Then he fled from the creek, and he didn't know why he fled. Perhaps he didn't want to see the splendid, spawned-out salmon die. Perhaps he didn't want to see the spent bodies cuffed out of the creek by the marauding bears. Or perhaps, most of all, he did not want to be tempted by the racing river.

He fled straight to the village.

"Come on, Lax!" he ordered his slave boy as soon as he reached home. "We'll catch one more eagle."

"But . . . but . . ." Lax held up his torn hands piteously. Eagles had needle-sharp talons.

"One more eagle!" the prince commanded.

Running lightly toward the eagle pit, neither noticed the four youths following stealthily at a distance.

"Into the pit!" Yaloa ordered.

Lax got into the pit and was concealed by the branches.

Standing on the poles across the pit, Yaloa noticed that the world was lovely. All along the nearby riverbank, the cottonwoods were gold in the autumn sunlight. The mountains were deeply, mistily blue behind the thrusting green of tall timbers. And the air was bracing. The river—

The river was calling to him.

He saw the eagle, circling high against the blue sky. "Chief of all the wild ones!" he muttered, reverently. And he watched its high flight with pure envy.

But the river was calling to him.

"NO!" he called back. He would never be a salmon —except for the few moments it took to entice an eagle.

But the song of the river seemed to swell into a wild call. And against his will, he listened to it. "Even the lordly eagle," it seemed to say, "even the lordly eagle is just a hungry guest, coming to the feast of the great Salmon People."

That was true, of course, but—

The river was still singing its wild song. "Even the lordly eagle," it seemed to say, "even the lordly eagle is just an eager guest, taking the gifts of the Great Chiefs, the Salmon People."

In his fancy, he saw again the stream of rosy, translucent eggs and the swift milt. The gift of life, of the life on which other life depended all along the river. Even the lordly eagle was a taker; and the honor was with the giver.

He looked skyward again, at the circling eagle. And now, for the first time, he saw it as just a hungry creature, dependent on the lordly salmon who gave the feast and the gifts so gloriously, who did what had to be done with grace and spirit. And who depended, in turn, on the grace and spirit of the beings they gave life to.

"You *are* all chiefs," he said again. "You are *all* chiefs." And he felt an overwhelming longing to go with them again on the great adventure.

Swiftly, before he could change his mind, Yaloa took the Stone of Safety out of his mouth. He stretched his arms wide to the world. Then, with grace and spirit, he tossed the pebble into the racing river and tapped his head lightly with the fish club.

Aghast at the events of the spring and summer, and alarmed now by the growing desperation of their prince, his four youths had crept stealthily close to the eagle pit, closer than they had come to any previous eagle catching.

Peering through concealing leaves and branches, they had seen him stand, as before, on the poles. They had heard him shout "NO!" to the river. They had seen him stretch his arms wide to the world. They had heard the *plop* of the pebble in the racing waters. They had watched, open mouthed, as he had tapped his head lightly. They had gasped when he had turned instantly into a small spring salmon. And they had held their breath, as always, while the eagle dived toward the living silver.

But this time the prince stayed a salmon.

And the fierce eagle struck him.

As one, the youths leaped, shouting, toward the eagle. And the great bird took flight without his victim.

Lax poked his head up through the branches. He gasped at the sight of the bleeding bait, then gave up and howled to relieve his feelings.

"Look!" one of the four youths said, pointing at the torn fish. "Copper."

"The prince's neck ring," another gasped, falling back in awe from the bleeding salmon.

"We'll get the shaman," a third said. "Quick! The shaman!" And he took off.

"But if the eagle comes back!" Lax screeched at him.

The fourth youth moved some branches to screen the enticing little salmon. Then he took off, after his friends.

Lax ran screeching behind them.

In a frenzy of excitement, the whole village followed the boys and the shaman back to the eagle pit. But when they got there, there was nothing. Just empty green branches warming in the autumn sunshine. The fish had vanished.

The tribe fell back in awe. And a low singing started. It started and then swelled into a wild lament for the lost prince of the Killer Whales.

Only one old, old shaman was still and silent, still and silent as though straining to hear something beyond the others' hearing.

People remembered this later, when rumors began to spread along the river. Rumors of a strange, silvery canoe that had slipped down the river as silently as a salmon.

The greatest of all the winter potlatches buzzed with the rumors. Chief Hay-il installed his younger sister's son as his heir. He gave magnificent gifts in the boy's honor. And eagle down floated over the brilliantly costumed dancers like a glorious fall of snow.

But the focus of interest was still the heir who had vanished, the heir who had not come to the potlatch. For a famous storyteller told and retold and retold the story of *The Prince Who Was Taken Away by the Salmon.*

THE WEALTH
OF STORY
ILLUSTRATION

When the people went home from the potlatch, they did not forget the stories.

How could they? When every house, every canoe, every fish club, box, bowl, or spoon they touched was elegantly decorated; and every decorative motif had come out of a myth or a tribal legend.

Any hour of any day their glance might fall on *The Prince Who Was Taken Away by the Salmon*, on *Thunderbird* who had carried off the whale, or on *The Wild Woman of the Woods* who had carried off the children. Their eyes might chance on *The One-Horned Mountain Goat* or on *Bear* or *Wolf* or *Beaver*. The flames of their lodge fire might brighten *Raven* who had spread fire over a cold world before he began to spread only mischief.

The magic of myth was all around them in a wealth of carving. And the carvings were startling yet exquisite, terrifying yet elegant. Legendary characters had been abstracted into a unique, sophisticated style that is still one of the world's great art styles. Animal forms had been distorted or compressed or broken up to fit them into the space allowed by the prow of a canoe or the handle of a horn spoon. Sometimes people could recognize the characters only by their identifying symbols.

The high dorsal fin that sliced through the ocean was the identifying symbol of *Killer Whale*. Lesser symbols were a large head, large teeth and a small, round blowhole. The fin and the blowhole could be placed anywhere in the carving. But they had to be there, somewhere. And since ears over the forehead were the identifying symbol of an animal, a Killer Whale carving depicted either the legendary sea monster or a human hero of the Killer Whale crest, depending on the presence or absence of the ears.

An enormous hooked beak, curved back to touch the chin, was the symbol of *Hawk*. If great wings had been added, then *Thunderbird* had been depicted. *Eagle* had a large curved beak too, but the point of his beak was turned downward. *Raven*'s beak went straight out.

Bear was symbolized by a large mouth set with many teeth, a protruding tongue, and large paws.

64

Wolf had many teeth too, but his eyes were slanted.

Two large incisors and a cross-hatched tail meant *Beaver*.

There were many, many story characters. And every one had his identifying symbols. The modern illustrator of this book was working in the authentic tradition of Northwest Coast art when he put Yaloa's own Killer Whale crest and his high-ranking hat on his new salmon body. They identified this salmon as the Killer Whale prince.

The prevalence of *Raven* in the Northwest's decoration suggests that the tales of The Trickster were widely popular. Perhaps, in a culture that forbade greed and gluttony, people enjoyed adventuring vicariously with the greediest of gluttons.

Their versions of *Raven*'s adventures were funnier than ours can be. For they were rich with little "in jokes," with having the character do a hundred little things that the people of the potlatch knew proper people would never do.

The old stories were also longer than ours. One famous Indian storyteller took three days to relate all the adventures of *Raven*. We can tell just a few.

RAVEN
TRAVELING

Once in the days of very long ago, the trickiest of all tricksters roamed the Northwest Coast, playing pranks on everybody. And people couldn't protect themselves from his pranks because they never knew it was Raven they were dealing with until after he had done the mischief.

Being supernatural, he could transform himself into whatever it suited him to be at the moment. He could appear to people as a handsome young chief, or as a bird, or as an ordinary everyday truth-telling traveler. And only when he had tricked them out of their food would they realize who he was.

Then . . . "It's The Trickster!" someone would cry out.

And everyone in the tribe would gasp, "Raven!"

Then they would all sag in despair and watch him fly off. For, at the last moment, he usually escaped in the form of a great glistening black bird.

Actually, it wasn't altogether Raven's fault that he was such a nuisance along the Northwest Coast. He did what he did because he, too, had been tricked. But to understand that, we need to go back to the beginning.

It was the very beginning, when people still moved about in the thin light of stars.

It was the very beginning of the world, when things had not settled down finally into being what they are now.

Yet some things were the same then.

In a village on a big offshore island, the head chief and his wife were as fond of their little son as any modern doting parents. And they were as foolishly indulgent. They gave him small bows and arrows and let him shoot the trusting little birds that were brightening up a dark world with song. Also, they pretended that he didn't eat nearly as much as he did eat.

"Pff!" his doting mother always said to relatives who were concerned that their prince should not shame them by becoming a greedy glutton in a world where food was hard to come by. "White Raven contents himself for days with merely chewing on a bit of goat fat."

68

"Then where did that salmon go?" the relatives always demanded. "And why aren't there more berries in the baskets after all that picking?"

"Why indeed!" the child's mother always answered with spirit. "Because that slave of his eats all he can get his hands on, pretending White Raven eats it. I think he must have a mouth at both ends."

"Mouth at both ends?" The relatives always went into such gales of laughter at the thought of a man with a mouth at both ends that they began to call the slave by that name. And the name stuck.

"Mouth-at-Both-Ends!" the slave fumed to his wife. "When I can't get enough to feed the mouth at one end, with that greedy child gobbling up everything in sight."

"Now, now, my dear," his wife comforted him. "What does a name matter to a slave? If you gained a reputation for eating as little as you actually do eat, people would say you were reaching above your station . . . trying to prove that you really are a prince snatched away as a child from your native village."

"Which I may be," the offended slave always retorted. Not that he minded about having been snatched away. His memory of his native village was very dim. Not only had he left it as a young child, but also, he seemed to remember, there had been no fire in that village. In his father's house across the sea where the stars rose, there had been no flames leaping up through the gloom, lifting people's hearts and wafting wonderful cooking smells past their eager noses. Still, he treasured the thought that perhaps he had been noble. "I do seem to have a natural tendency to eat as lightly as a prince," he often said to his wife.

"As lightly as a *prince?*" she usually joked in answer.

Then, one day, when the prince was growing into a tall youth, he shot a heaven bird—a large, radiant, white bird with a long beak of pure copper.

People trembled with fear.

Shamans danced and rattled up a frenzy.

Even the prince's mother seemed a bit alarmed. Yet, when her son coaxed her, she skinned the heaven bird to make a beautiful white feather cloak with a bird headpiece. A headpiece with a long glinting beak of copper.

Now the relatives were really anxious. "Wearing a heaven bird in play!" they said, aghast.

Perhaps they were actually relieved when the boy took sick and died.

Certainly the slave was. "Best thing that could have happened," Mouth-at-Both-Ends told his wife. "There's no telling what wrath he might have brought down on the village."

His kind wife almost agreed. By now, even she was aghast at what the doting mother had done, and was still doing. Now she was having the prince stuffed with shredded-cedar bark and laid out on a sleeping platform so that the village might never stop wailing over what it had lost.

"Of course it's not unusual to stuff a noble," the slave's wife remarked.

"Just unusually appropriate," Mouth-at-Both-Ends retorted. "When the prince finally stops stuffing himself, someone else stuffs him."

What was unusual was the wailing.

"Wailing forever for a prince who was nothing but trouble!" Mouth-at-Both-Ends protested.

"Now, now, my dear," his wife scolded gently. "Perhaps she doesn't expect it to be forever. Maybe she thinks he'll come back to life."

The villagers almost began to hope he would, just so they could be free of the everlasting wailing. Their world was gloomy enough as it was.

Yet they were stunned when he actually did wake up one day and rise up from his sleeping platform. They fell back in awe, eyes wide and mouths wider.

"It's not the prince," an old, old woman muttered. "A spirit child has dropped from the sky and entered into the body of the dead prince."

Certainly the newly risen prince did seem to have a radiance he had not had before. Also, he did not shoot any pretty little song birds.

"This is not the prince," Mouth-at-Both-Ends told his wife, positively. "He doesn't eat at all."

And that was true. He did not even seem to chew fat.

"Only a spirit child could go without food at all,"

the slave insisted.

"Now, now, my dear," his wife disagreed gently. "It's the prince. It's just that, at long last, he has come into his true nobility. He has finally become what he always should have been. It just took him a little while to grow up."

"I'll think what I think," her husband answered. "But I won't talk about it." He did not want to re-start the wailing. "I'll just watch."

White Raven—if indeed it was White Raven—did not even prance about any more in his heaven-bird cloak.

The sharp eyed people noticed all these things. But they pretended to believe that this was White Raven, returned to his sorrowing tribe. Perhaps they, too, were afraid of being ordered back to more wailing for the greedy little glutton who had shot the song birds.

The awe with which the villagers now treated their prince merely delighted his doting mother.

But the relatives were not so blinded. "This can't be the prince," they told one another. "Look! No salmon are mysteriously disappearing. No berries are ever missing now from the baskets."

When such words reached the mother's ears, she answered them with spirit. "No salmon are mysteriously disappearing now, and no berries are ever missing from the baskets, because Mouth-at-Both-Ends has learned his lesson."

"But she hasn't learned hers," the slave muttered.

"Now, now," she soothed. "What does it matter?"

The slave thought it did matter. It was bad enough being a slave without being the butt of all the food jokes in the village, too. And he was naturally curious to know if this radiant boy really was the prince, or if he really was a spirit child using the prince's body.

By and by, he began to think that maybe it was the prince after all. The boy kept asking him about food.

"Why do you look so happy when you eat?" the shining youth wanted to know, again and again. "What does food taste like?"

Sometimes the slave scowled at these questions, thinking that it was the old prince, meanly making fun of the slave. "His mind is always on food, even if his teeth aren't," he told his wife. "It's the old prince."

"But no!" he said one day, struck by a notion. "Perhaps even a spirit child can be infected by the gluttony of the body he is wearing."

In those days, people believed in contagious magic. They believed that any part of a thing held the essence of the whole thing, and that that essence was contagious. Clearly, any bit of a river held the wetness of the whole river; and a man caught that wetness himself if he touched it. Similarly, people reasoned, if a man tied a bear claw around his neck or drank a bit of the bear's blood, he was infected with the great strength of the bear. If he put an eagle feather into his hair, he caught the grace and speed of the eagle.

So Mouth-at-Both-Ends reasoned that, if a spirit child were wearing the gluttonous prince's body, even he was bound to become infected with gluttony.

More and more, the slave was convinced that this was what was happening. For, more and more, White Raven simply could not keep his mind off food. He kept asking how things tasted. Yet when his anxious mother urged him to eat, he fled from her as though from a terrible temptation.

"A spirit child knows he must not eat earthly food," the slave guessed. But by and by, he was too annoyed to care. For it seemed to him that whenever the boy wasn't hounding him with questions about food, the boy's mother was hounding him with orders about it.

"Have your wife prepare his food more temptingly!" she ordered. "The prince will die again if you don't get some food into him. So tell your wretched wife that she will get the prince eating . . . or. . . ."

It was the angry "or" that settled the matter for Mouth-at-Both-Ends. His dear wife was being threatened. And since she was only a slave, like himself, she could be staked out in the rising tide if it suited her angry mistress.

"We'll make him eat," Mouth-at-Both-Ends stormed to his wife one day. And he snatched up a fragrant roasted grouse. But, leaping at the pain of burned fingers, he cracked a sore shin against the end

74

of a firelog, and nearly knocked a scab off it.

"That's it!" he yelled in grim triumph, wrenching the scab free. He thrust it deep into the cooked grouse and regarded it with dark glittering eyes.

"But—my dear!" his wife gasped. "You can't feed the prince a scab."

"A scab from a slave's body!" Mouth-at-Both-Ends gloated. A scab holding the essence of slavishness the way an eagle feather held the essence of grace and speed. "Why not? Why can't I put a bit of ME into HIM? It's time that arrogant line of his was infected with humility."

And when the prince arrived, some minutes later, sniffing the aroma of hot food with wild-eyed longing, Mouth-at-Both-Ends pushed the slightly cooled grouse into his hand. Then he pushed the hand up close to the yearning nose. "There! Taste that!"

In sheer surprise the shining prince tasted it. First, he touched the roasted grouse with his tongue. He licked it ravenously. Then, closing his eyes as if in bliss, he really sank his teeth into the luscious, juicy, fragrant grouse. And he ate every scrap of it. He greedily chewed on the bones and licked his fingers. And then, flinging the bones from him with one piercing cry, he raced away in panic.

"My dear!" the slave's wife gasped. "What have you done to him?"

It was soon very clear what the slave had done to him.

It was as if the contagious magic of the ignoble scab and the gluttonous body had combined with the terrible power of a supernatural being. White Raven became a slave to an insatiable appetite. He became the most ravenous glutton the world has ever suffered. He had to have food, no matter how he got it.

At first, it was no problem. Delighted to see her adored son eating at last, his doting mother plied him with meat and fish and berries.

But soon there were no meat and fish and berries left in his father's house. So the prince raced around to the other houses demanding food. And because he was the highest-ranking boy in the village, no one dared to refuse him.

"He shames us!" the relatives wailed.

"He'll sicken himself and die again!" his mother sobbed.

It was his father, the head chief, who stopped him. Saddened and shamed by his son's gluttony, he called the tribe together. For his first duty was to the people.

"Great Tribe!" he said to the people. "I will send my dear child away before he eats all our provisions and brings us to starvation."

The people agreed with public wails of dismay and private whoops of delight.

"My dear son," the head chief said quietly to White Raven while his wife wept, "I shall send you away across the water." He pointed eastward toward the big land. Then, taking the heaven-bird cloak out

76

of a carved chest, he handed it to the boy.

White Raven put it on, fitting the headpiece carefully over his own shining head. And being supernatural, he instantly caught the feathers' flying magic.

As he tried his wings, his face brightened. With wings, he could really find food.

"Food!" he shouted, flashing his enormous beak in the firelight.

And without one backward glance, he soared up and away.

Raven had started traveling.

There was one small delay in getting food. White Raven hadn't traveled far into the big, gloomy, mountainous land across the water before he realized that if only there were more light in the land, there would be more goats hunted and more berries picked and more fish landed. In short, there would be more food for him to make off with.

He did not really consider hunting and fishing and gathering berries for himself. The people could do that better.

So, remembering the light in the Sky Land he had once fallen out of, he made straight for the Hole in the Sky. And before anyone up there realized who he was or what he was after, he had made off with a small Sun and had dropped back down through the Hole in the Sky.

The people below were stunned by the sudden brightness. They were awed by the heat and light in their previously cold, dim world. And when they really saw the wealth of game and fruit around them, they threw themselves joyously into hunting and fishing and gathering roots and berries.

White Raven threw himself even more joyously into stealing what they hunted and fished and gathered, growing bigger and bigger as he gorged himself on others' food.

Still, every time he sank his teeth into a raw, cold fish, he thought of the lovely hot steaming red-and-silver salmon in his father's house. Every time he bit into a piece of raw cold meat, he remembered the succulent grouse Mouth-at-Both-Ends' wife had prepared for him. And his mouth watered and watered and watered. His tongue licked his lips longingly.

At last, he could stand it no longer.

"Great Tribe!" he called out to the very next village that tried to drive him off. "I am the one who brought you the light from Sky Land. And now I am ready to bring you fire from my father's village across the water."

"Fire?" they asked him, curious enough to forget their anger for the moment.

When he told them what fire was and what it could do for them, they eagerly fed him all they had left to strengthen him for the journey.

White Raven flew off happily. He knew that his parents, and especially his doting mother, would gladly give him fire. But as he neared the old village on the offshore island, he saw scores of people rushing down to the beach with raised fists and sticks and stones and even harpoons and bows and arrows. He simply could not get close enough to ask his mother.

So he flew dolefully and hungrily back over the water.

Resting on a halfway island, he watched an enormous flock of gulls with greedy interest. What great food-getters they were! But why did they keep dropping clams behind a big rock?

Moving as a huge youth with his feather cloak tucked under one arm, White Raven looked behind the big rock. And his mouth opened in sheer envy. For there sat a young man, eating, while the gulls dropped an endless supply of food to him.

White Raven's eyes brightened with hope. Here

was a worthy companion, someone voracious like himself but with better food arrangements.

"You live well," he remarked, approaching the stranger with a disarming smile.

"Well enough," the young man answered warily. And he stopped eating long enough to tuck his own flying blanket in closer to his body. For this was Sea Gull, a supernatural youth like White Raven, with his own magical cloak of feathers.

"You would like to live better?" White Raven suggested, dropping down beside the well-fed stranger.

"You know how to live better?" Sea Gull asked him, gesturing toward the busy gulls.

"Much better," White Raven said, putting out his hand to catch some of the clams the birds were dropping. "I have lived better in my father's village." And he began to talk of fragrant steamed clams, and succulent salmon, and luscious roasted meat with such heartfelt longing that Sea Gull's mouth began to water. His tongue began to lick his lips.

Finally, Sea Gull leaped to his feet. "What are we waiting for?" he demanded, snatching up his supernatural flying blanket, which was smaller and grayer than White Raven's heaven-bird cloak.

"For a good plan," White Raven answered. And he told Sea Gull a fantastic lie about a wicked relative who had cheated him out of his rightful place in the village and had turned a loving people against their true noble prince. "So I'll have to disguise myself to get back into the village," he said. "And then we'll have to snatch the fire and run for it."

Driven by their craving for cooked food, the two soon had their plan ready. Sea Gull's supernatural friend Shark would lend them his canoe so that they could arrive at the village without arousing suspicion. And he himself would pretend to be the attendant of a great young chief who wished to keep his identity secret for the moment and who would reveal himself only after he had performed his ceremonial dance for the people of the village.

Since Shark's canoe was supernatural like himself, it was easily pulled through the sea by Sea Gull's birds, each with a kelp line in his beak. And before long, the two gluttonous plotters neared the village on the big offshore island.

It was early morning when the villagers saw the strange canoe, almost lost in its blizzard of birds. They blinked their eyes against the brightness of the rising sun. But even when the mysterious craft drew near the shore, they could not make out many details. The high prow did seem to display a Shark totem, and occasionally a figure moved behind it. But since the birds never settled for a moment, the glimpses were merely tantalizing.

Then a handsome young man swam ashore from it. And his manners were very proper.

"Great Chiefs!" Sea Gull hailed the village. "Great Tribe! A famous and handsome young chief wishes to visit you tonight. And he wishes to introduce himself in a dance. Only when he has delighted your young men and your young women with his performance will he reveal himself as someone you have honored on other occasions."

"A famous young chief?" the men said, eagerly scanning the sea against the sunrise.

"A handsome young chief?" the women said, eagerly scanning their marriageable daughters.

That was it, they all decided when the stranger had swum off. A famous and handsome young chief was looking for a wife. So they threw themselves into preparations for the evening. Logs were piled for a great leaping fire in the head chief's house. Food was readied. And festive regalia was shaken out in the lively breezes.

Lost in its blizzard of birds, the mysterious canoe disappeared behind a nearby island. And nobody saw the gulls feeding the two gluttons. Nobody saw the craft slip westward among the islands so that it could appear again against the blinding sunset.

As the sun sank, fires were lighted along the beach and people chanted a joyous welcome.

It was nearly dark when the strangers stepped ashore. And they moved in such a blizzard of birds that no one got close enough to notice that there were no paddlers. All eyes were on the noble visitors as the Shark canoe slipped well offshore again.

Sea Gull wore a dancing blanket he had borrowed

with the canoe. It rattled with sharks' teeth and glittered with pearl shell.

White Raven was dressed as a famous land-hunter might dress for a ceremonial dance—in deerhide and antlers. He rattled with deer hoof fringes. And his long tail—for deer had long tails then—was strangely stiffened. People were too excited about the costume and the huge figure inside it to notice that the tail had been stiffened by lashing it to a length of pitchwood, the kind of pitchwood they used for torches.

The villagers trooped excitedly into the big house. Then sitting well back from the leaping fire, they beat time with their sticks and chanted as the visiting prince began his fantastic deer dance.

Prancing as a great young stag might prance, he circled closer and closer to the fire in the center of the feasthouse. Then, tossing his antlered head high, he moved his tail so close to the flames that it caught fire.

People gasped. But the prince danced on as though this was part of the performance. Which it certainly was. He danced on until he neared the entry hole in the portal crestpole of the great house. Then he darted out, with Sea Gull right behind him.

Startled by his exit, people waited for a few minutes. But when the visitor did not reappear, they streamed out into the night after him. They were just in time to see their two honored guests jump on board their mysterious craft and glide off in a blizzard of birds. Then their mouths dropped open. For, suddenly, a gigantic bird rose from the canoe, carrying a firebrand in its beak—in its glinting beak of pure copper.

"White Raven!" they gasped, furious at having been tricked.

Saddened and shamed all over again, the head chief sagged with dismay.

His wife burst into renewed wailing for her lost darling, while the villagers eyed her anxiously in case she should order them to renew their wailing too.

Mouth-at-Both-Ends shook his fist after the retreating trickster.

"Now, now, my dear," his wife soothed him. "Don't begrudge the prince a little fire for the chilly evenings."

The minute White Raven reached the halfway island, he struck a tree with his firebrand to let the tree catch the essence of fire. "Keep fire safe as long as the years last!" he ordered.

And it was fortunate that he did that. For the pitchwood burned out long before he had stirred himself to get a little fuel to keep it going.

"The fire's gone!" Sea Gull gasped as he watched the flame flicker out.

"Not from your clever friend," White Raven assured him. And he broke off two sticks from the tree. "Give up some fire!" he ordered.

But the tree, none too pleased by White Raven's manner, gave up some fire only after making him coax it from the sticks with a lot of effort. And even then it came up in such sparse sparks that the too-demanding fellow had to hustle to get his fire going.

"This is too much work," Sea Gull said, every time they had to rekindle their fire to cook food.

"Because your gulls don't know how to keep the fire going," White Raven always retorted. "Besides, they're not very good food providers, either. They never bring in deer or mountain goat, gleaming salmon or juicy berries, or a plump grouse or a bit of whale blubber or. . . ." He always had to stop himself before he tore his hair out in frenzy, thinking about all the fragrant, luscious food he was missing.

"I promised fire to a village," he announced one day, suddenly remembering his promise now that he needed hunters and berry-pickers and fishermen.

Sea Gull hid his satisfaction, in case his friend should change his mind and not go.

White Raven put on his feather cloak and flew off with two fire sticks. And just because people were such suspicious beings, he took the precaution of kindling a good flame before he approached the village.

The suspicious people crowding the village beach dropped their sticks and stones and spears and bows and arrows as they watched him walk in with the flaming torch. "That's fire," they guessed, correctly. And they crowded excitedly around him while he showed them how to feed it to make the fire big.

Then he showed them how to cook food.

"I'd better see if you're doing it right," he kept saying as he tasted the food and tasted the food again. "Mmmmmmmmmm!" he kept saying, cocking his head to consider. "Perhaps . . . a bit more."

Somehow the food never seemed to be quite ready for them to try it. And salmon after salmon disappeared in the testing. Roast after roast of venison vanished into the taster . . . while fragrant cooking smells wafted past yearning noses . . . and mouths watered . . . and tongues began to lick lips.

Suddenly one sharp-eyed old man could stand it no longer. "Trickster!" he yelled.

And as though with a single mind, all the people raced to the spot where they had dropped their sticks and stones and spears and bows and arrows. Suspicious once more, they moved menacingly toward White Raven.

"You ungrateful wretches!" he said. "When I came only to give you a way to have cooked food."

"When you came only to give *you* a way to have cooked food," a sharp-tongued woman answered. "Be on your way, trickster!"

"But I'll starve!" White Raven protested.

"You will or we will," the people retorted. And with such a simple decision to make, they raised their sticks and spears so menacingly he decided that maybe he wanted to go traveling again after all.

Word of fire swept over the land like a wild wind. In a dozen villages the prince and his fire sticks were hailed with delight, only to be chased off again before he had cleaned out the winter's provisions.

Usually, the weather made him demonstrate the cooking inside the great cedar houses. So he often had to escape by flight through the new smoke holes people were arranging in their roofs. In fact, he got stuck so often in the make-shift smoke holes that his feathers were soon blackened. And people began to call him Raven, rather than White Raven.

He was quite black and quite tired of fire sticks by the time he spotted a stranded whale from the air. It

was drifting toward a beach in front of a village.

He was, in fact, so black that curious flocks of crows and ravens had gathered around him. And this combined flock of black birds flew down with him to hover over the drifting carcass.

The villagers were gathered on the beach, waiting for the carcass to drift right in. They were eagerly considering the prospect of a great winter's supply of whale meat and whale oil.

It was a prospect that appealed equally to Raven. And being a very tricky fellow, he soon thought of a way to make the whale his own.

Since he had never before approached a village in the form of a large black bird, but always as a young man, he knew that the villagers would not be suspicious.

They were merely astounded to see so enormous a raven lead his tribe in several low circles over the drifting whale, screaming something in the raven language.

"*Gulâge gag dze el ban!*" they heard him cry out again and again to his followers.

They saw the flock of birds hesitate each time, then finally flutter about in indecision.

"What is it? What is it?" the villagers asked one another.

"*Gulâge gag dze el ban!*" the enormous raven screamed at the birds, once more, very fiercely.

And that time the flock took off. Like a black streak, it flew off up the wild coast.

"What's the matter?" people wondered, their eyes fixed on the enormous bird.

Now he lighted on a big rock near them. *"Gulâge gag dze el ban!"* he screamed at them, flapping his wings fiercely.

But no one in the village understood the raven language. They only knew it must be something about the whale. And they began to eye the floating carcass with some concern. Perhaps . . . perhaps the shamans could find out something.

The shamans put on their bear-claw crowns and their dancing aprons. They shook their rattles. They danced in frenzy. But, by morning, they still did not know what the raven words meant.

In fact, the villagers were gathered in small anxious knots on the beach when a strange young man came along. He had lost his way, hunting, he told them.

He, too, looked at the whale, which by then was stranded on the beach. "Why are you not cutting whale meat?" he asked them.

It was because of what a huge raven had said, they told him.

"A raven?" the stranger asked with growing interest. "A raven is very wise. What did he tell you?"

"We could not understand him," the people admitted.

"Then I'm sorry I was not here. I know the raven language."

Everyone crowded around him. And half a dozen people could repeat the raven's exact words, even if they did not know their meaning."

90

"Not . . . '*Gulâge gag dze el ban!*' " the stranger cried out, clapping his hand to his head as if in dismay.

"That's exactly what he said, and exactly how he said it," people told him. And they waited with anxious, wide eyes to have the words translated.

"You're sure?" the stranger asked, as though reluctant to believe it. "You're sure he said, '*Gulâge gag dze el ban!*'?"

The villagers were as sure as ever, and twice as anxious. "What does it mean?" they implored the young man.

Seeming most hesitant to give them the bad news, the young man translated the raven's words. "*A pestilence will come to this village in a few days.*"

"PESTILENCE?" People eyed the whale in horror. "Why?" they asked, drawing back in dread from the carcass.

"I can't tell you why," the stranger answered. "I only know what the raven said. But the raven is very wise. He must know something."

Perhaps the whale had touched the Land of Pestilence, people suggested in horror.

"*Gulâge gag dze el ban!*" the stranger repeated, as though to consider it once more. And he said it so exactly as the enormous bird had said it that people saw again the panicked flight of the birds, away from the floating carcass.

"Great Tribe!" the head chief called out. "We will move out as the sun rises tomorrow morning." He ordered a slave to run about, crying, "Great Tribe! Leave!"

The stranger did not wait for morning to leave. He disappeared at once around a headland and was not seen again.

The enormous raven came back, though. He came back just long enough to alight again on the rock, flap his wings fiercely, and scream, "*Gulâge gag dze el ban!*"

"We're leaving. We're leaving," people told him. And they hurried to pack their things.

As the sun rose the next morning, they were too busy getting away to notice Raven, high in a tree. But he saw their hasty flight from the village. His bright eyes followed their canoes as far as a bird could see them. Then he flew down to the beach, took off his flying cloak, and settled in for a cozy winter.

The prospect of months of gorging himself on food spurred him to carve up the carcass and store the meat and fat in the empty houses.

It was just his misfortune that rumors of fire were not the only rumors sweeping the land. Rumors of Raven's tricks, too, were spreading so far and so fast that they soon reached the ears of the fleeing villagers.

One of the villagers, even more suspicious than the others, slipped back to the village one day. And he saw what he half expected. The concerned stranger who had translated the raven words was gorging himself on whale meat.

Days later the tribe returned. And the purposeful dip of their paddles told Raven that it was once more time to travel.

"And after I did all the work!" he muttered, with considerable indignation.

Never one to waste a good idea, Raven used almost the same trick to frighten another tribe away from its supply of codfish. And for some time, he lived luxuriously.

Then his tricks began to fail, mainly because people were getting wise to him. In fact, he grew so hungry that he actually took to stealing the bait off fish hooks, down deep in the water. And it was only after nearly losing his jaw as well as his dignity that he gave up this style of dining.

He was desperate with hunger the day he encountered some children.

He was so fuddled with hunger as he staggered toward the cooking smells of a village that he did not even notice it was the village he had once cheated out of its whale with his "*Gulâge gag dze el ban!*" trick.

He found himself near the end of the town where the children were playing. And it was what they were playing with that roused him from his stupor. They were playing catch with balls of whale blubber.

"Blubber! Blubber!" he blubbered, suddenly wild-eyed with hope. And he managed to move among the children and catch their balls and eat them so craftily that the children kept thinking they were losing them in the nearby trees and in the ocean.

Except for one big, bright-eyed boy who was watching the stranger closely. And when all the balls had disappeared and all the other children were glancing about in puzzlement, he moved out among them, nudging and winking and whispering, "It's The Trickster."

After a few final nudges and winks and whispers, he pointed to a tall tree. "Want me to go up and get some more balls?" he asked the children, in a seemingly offhand manner.

Raven, fuddled by faintness and caught up in a terrible craving for food, asked, "Where do you get your blubber?"

The boy jumped in with his answer before anyone else could speak up. "Oh, we climb that tree and throw ourselves down from the top. Then, before we hit the ground, we shout, 'High piles of blubber!' And, instantly, there they are for us to land in—high piles of blubber."

"*High* piles of blubber?" Raven asked. His mouth watering. "High *piles* of blubber?"

Catching on to their friend's plot, all the children nodded in agreement. "High piles of blubber!" they told Raven.

"You mean . . . you climb that tree. Throw yourself down from the top, and land in high piles of blubber?"

94

"That's all there is to it," the boy assured him, while his playmates kept a straight face.

"Well . . ." Raven went on, after licking his lips a few more times, "when are you going to do it?"

"Oh . . ." the boy answered with a shrug, "one of these days . . . some time when we happen to feel like playing the game again."

"But . . . but . . . but. . . ." Raven swallowed his despair as the children started ambling away toward the houses. Then he staggered toward the tree himself, his eyes glittering like a madman's. "You say, 'High piles of blubber!'?"

"High piles of blubber." The boy stopped walking and glanced back as he confirmed it.

"High piles of blubber," the rest of the children chimed in.

Then, wide-eyed with amazement at his stupidity, they watched the stranger scramble up the high tree. They saw him hurl himself off the top. And they caught his two words, "High piles. . . ." before he landed. Not in high piles of blubber.

"Serves him right," the big boy said, blustering a little as he looked down at the fallen figure.

"He did it himself," another piped up, though a little weakly.

"He won't starve out another village," others agreed, bolstering their sinking courage before they raced off to face their parents.

But when the unbelieving villagers trooped back

to the tree with the children to see, the stranger had vanished.

Raven, supernatural, immortal, and outwitted by a pack of children, had shamefacedly resumed his traveling.

The affair of the blubber made Raven grow more crafty.

"If you can't even trust children!" he muttered, with righteous indignation.

If he couldn't even trust children any more, then he simply had to be more tricky to protect himself. So his plans began to be much more complicated.

He had been given a bottomless belly through no fault of his own, he reasoned, and also the wits to fill it now and then. He had been handed an endless challenge. And it was his job to rise nobly to that challenge.

That was his excuse the day he kicked a princess.

That incident happened this way:

He was desperately hungry the day he found himself on a trail at the edge of a large village. Peering warily through the trees, he saw that the houses were big and magnificently carved with the owners' emblems. The canoes drawn up along the riverbank were brilliant with painted totems. His first glance told him that this village would be exceptionally well provisioned.

It was just his misfortune that people were such suspicious beings that a man could not simply walk right up and expect a welcome.

Thinking of the welcome that might have been, his mouth began to water. Thinking of fragrant food on a fresh mat by the fire, his tongue began to lick his lips. And his wits began to work, especially after he saw a princess and her four maidens go off in a canoe with their berry baskets.

"Off to the berry patches!" he noted, gleefully rubbing his hands together. "Berries!" Sweet, luscious, juicy, fragrant blueberries! he thought. If only he could sit down with five big baskets full of sweet, luscious, juicy, fragrant blueberries!

Then his eyes went wide and bright. With a little clever planning, there could be much, much more in it for him than five baskets of berries. He slipped back along the trail with such a fabulous plan that he was even willing to do a little work.

First he put on his flying cloak and flew off to see which way the girls were going and to find a deer. What he was planning, he told himself, was nothing more than rising nobly to the challenge of his misfortune.

By a little silent soaring, he managed to alight close to a stag with a good spread of antlers. With silent trickery, he turned back into a huge man and overcame the surprised buck.

Then, wrinkling his nose in distaste for work, he

carefully skinned the deer. By the time he had it
skinned, of course, he had attended to the meat too
by disposing of it down his gullet.

Raven was tempted to just sit back and enjoy the
comfort of a moderately well-filled belly. But, thinking of the many well-filled bellies he had in mind, he
stirred himself into action.

A master of disguise by this time, he had completely disguised himself as a stag and was swimming
in the river by the time the girls came along with
their baskets of berries.

They bent to their paddles to give chase, as he had
intended. They soon caught up with him, as he also
had planned. And, excited by the prospect of out-
doing some young braggart village hunter, they hit
the buck with their paddles.

"We've killed him!" they gasped, as he had known
they would.

"So haul me into the canoe!" he said in a way that made the girls think they were hearing a spirit voice.

And the five girls did haul him into the canoe, as he had planned. A little unnerved, they paddled anxiously toward the village.

Craftily watching his chance, the stag suddenly kicked out with a hind leg, catching the princess—hard—in the stomach.

She doubled up in pain, groaning. Then, as her girls crowded around her, she fainted.

The stag leaped back into the river, with only one longing look at the baskets of berries.

Aghast at what had happened to their princess, the girls picked up their paddles again and raced home. Her father, the head chief, called in the village wise men. But they could do nothing for her. Then he called in the shamans from nearby villages. But they could do nothing either. The princess only seemed to grow worse.

She was very ill indeed when the strange canoe appeared on the river.

"Another shaman!" people guessed, noting the long, straggly hair of the man in the middle. "Perhaps he can cure our princess."

"Perhaps I can," the grizzled stranger agreed when he had stepped ashore at the village. He motioned his paddlers away. And the people, streaming hopefully into the head chief's house behind the newest shaman, did not see the canoe glide away around a bend in

the river. They did not see the paddlers change back
into the crows and ravens they really were. Nor did
they see those crows and ravens each pick up a beak-
ful of small white pebbles from the bottom of the
canoe and then perch on the head chief's roof, ready
for their next performance.

The newly arrived shaman graciously accepted a
little nourishment before he began his performance.
Then he opened the medicine chest a young man had
carried in for him. Taking out charcoal, he blackened his face. He put on his shaman's crown of
grizzly bear claws and neck ring of shredded red-
cedar bark. He put on the dancing apron that rattled
with tiny deer hoofs. He shook his big medicine rattle and beat on his board with his carved sticks before
he began his singing.

He sang a strange song, with his arms reaching up-
ward and his face turned up toward his Spirit Power.
And the house hushed itself to catch the strange
words:

*Let the mighty hail fall on the roof of this chief's
house!*
On the roof of this chief's house!
ON THE ROOF OF THIS CHIEF'S HOUSE!

Suddenly, the hail hit the roof like a storm of
white pebbles. It bounced on the roof like the bounc-
ing of small stones. And the tribe fell back in awe.

They edged away from a shaman with such mighty power. Then, almost holding their breath, they watched the stranger touch the princess on the spot where the stag had kicked her, and say, "Be cured, wound under the right ribs!"

And the wound was cured. The princess sat up and smiled, while the great house echoed with the voices of the happy people.

They pressed food on the awesome stranger. And they were so eager to repay him for his deed that they had only indulgent smiles for his awesome hunger.

Then the head chief spoke. "Ask me whatever you wish, and I will give it to you."

The house rang with approval. And the head chief spoke again in a loud, clear voice, for all to witness his promise to the stranger.

"Whatever you may ask me, I will give it to you, my dear good and true supernatural man—you who are possessed of supernatural powers; for you have succeeded in restoring my only daughter."

The stranger looked around at the witnesses to the head chief's promise. Then he, too, spoke in a loud, clear voice.

"What I want is that you should move and leave me all the provisions you have, for my young men have nothing. We have no time to obtain our own provisions, for we are going around all the time healing those who need us."

"You have my promise," the head chief assured him. And he sent slaves round the village crying, "Leave, Great Tribe! And leave your provisions behind you!"

The head chief had promised. And the whole tribe had witnessed his promise.

So he and his people left the village the next morning. They left all their food behind them. And when they had gone, Raven gorged himself on food. Then he took a walk, planning to gorge himself again, with renewed appetite, when he returned.

But when he returned, he found that his crows and ravens and all their relatives had already been into the food.

"Can't a great man trust anyone any more?" he angrily demanded of them.

Still, it was a long, lovely, lazy time before Raven had to resume his traveling.

He had been traveling the world for a long, long time when he chanced on a hut on a beach edging the dark, timbered mountains.

"Aha!" he thought. "Lonely people are always glad to see a stranger."

So, after hiding his too-well-known feather cloak, he presented himself as a tired and hungry traveler, which he was, and as a fine, handsome young man, which he had not been for some time.

He was welcomed into the hut even more warmly

than he had expected, and he was fed even more bountifully. For the people living there were an industrious widow and her beautiful daughter.

"Aha!" Raven told himself gleefully. "With a little careful planning, there can be more in this for me than just a good feed in passing."

A plan began to form in his crafty mind.

"You are well supplied with food," he noted with carefully concealed greed. "Yet there is no man to hunt and fish for you."

The widow sighed, ever so softly; yet Raven caught the weariness in her soft sigh. "Anything men can do, we can do," she told him with spirit. "Still. . . ." Her gaze ranged so wistfully over his stalwart, muscled body that he knew his next trick was going to be easy.

He opened his mouth as if with a sudden thought. "Perhaps I—" He stopped, as though hesitant to foist himself impulsively on the two lone women. Then he plunged on with a fantastic lie about a wicked relative who had done him out of his rightful place in his village. And not until he saw sympathy glowing warmly in the women's eyes did he make his offer.

"I would like to marry your daughter," he said to the widow, "and spend the rest of my life providing for her and for her beautiful mother."

After a few proper hesitations, the widow agreed gladly. For she was very tired of hunting and fishing as well as doing her own woman's work; yet she did not want to go back to the village where she would have had to marry her dead husband's brother, a man she did not like.

The daughter agreed, too, though a little more shyly. And for a few days, they feasted to celebrate the marriage.

Then Raven, seeing that now he was expected to work, made another delightful offer. "I will build a canoe at once," he said. "Then there will be one to take me off hunting and fishing, and one to take you to the berry patches."

The women thought it a splendid idea, especially when the young man went on to say, "The new canoe will be for you, my beautiful mother-in-law, while I will make do with your old one." And he gave them an enticing word picture of a small canoe rubbed to a shining smoothness and painted with the widow's most cherished emblems. "When your relatives see you in your new canoe," he craftily suggested, "they will see that you are doing well."

Obviously excited by the canoe he was going to make, he pointed to a lovely offshore island. "And when we have no work to do, we will go round the island together. You can sit listening to the birds and watching the salmon leap, while I do all the paddling."

They could hardly wait for him to start work on such a glorious pleasure craft.

"First, I must find the right cedar tree," he reminded them. "A fine straight cedar, not too big and not too small."

"I'll help you find it," his wife eagerly offered.

"No, no, no," he protested. "I plan to give you a surprise." Then, smiling tenderly at her, he went on, "But since I may have to walk a very long way, searching. . . ."

"You must eat well before you go," his wife said.

"And take something with you," her mother added.

"Well . . . if you insist, my dears."

Of course they insisted. "And we will have rich, hot, thick salmon soup waiting for you when you get back," they promised. Fortunately, they had a plentiful supply of dried salmon. As Raven had noted.

He managed to make the search for the right tree last for several days. He might have made it last longer if his young wife had not shown so much eagerness to help him.

"No, no, no," he protested again and again. "I plan to give you a surprise." Which was true. He did plan to give them a surprise.

"My dears!" he announced that very evening. "At last, I have found the tree. And now I will make the chips fly. I will work like ten beavers to finish the canoe quickly."

"Well . . . since you are going to work so hard," the women said, "you must eat well before you go, and you must take something with you."

"If you insist, my dears."

Of course they insisted. And day after day after day, they sang happily as they dug roots and gathered fruit to eke out their dwindling stores of provisions.

"He will soon have the canoe finished," they assured each other as time went by. And they cocked an ear to catch the far-away sounds of his busy stone axe. "He will soon be free to go hunting."

But as the time went on and on and on, anxious notes crept into the women's voices. The provisions were vanishing like snow near a hot fire. Yet neither wanted to spoil the young man's happiness in the surprise he was planning for them. They could hear his axe; and when they couldn't hear it, they knew he was working with the sharkskin he had taken, rubbing some part to smoothness. Still—the last of the dried salmon was rapidly disappearing.

The usual sounds of his axe had just started the morning the widow finally decided that they simply had to do something. "Your husband is so excited about his surprise for us," she told her daughter, "that he has never even noticed how low the food is getting. Yet he needs to eat, too, to work like ten beavers. So he may have to leave the canoe for a while to go off hunting and fishing."

The girl was most reluctant to spoil his plans. "Perhaps he is nearly finished," she said.

"If only we knew for sure," her mother answered.

"My dear . . . you must go and see."

"But—"

"He need never know that you have been there."
The widow opened the empty food boxes and
pointed to the empty walls and beams to point up
their plight. "Just slip through the woods and see if
he is nearly finished."

"Well . . ." her daughter agreed. "Perhaps if I
went stealthily enough. . . ."

And off she went. Guided by the sounds of the
stone axe, she slipped swiftly along the beach and
then followed her husband's path through the forest.
Finally, she reached the spot where she could see him.

Only he wasn't working.

He was lolling against a log, chewing on some fat,
while he tapped lazily against a hollow cedar. It was
the hollowness of the cedar that made the sounds
loud enough to carry all the way to the hut and the
listening women.

Realizing the truth, the girl gasped. Then she
raced back to tell her mother.

"So!" the indignant woman snorted. "So that is
how he provides for his wife and his beautiful
mother-in-law! While he eats us out of house and
home. That is how he surprises us! Well! Maybe we
can surprise the surpriser. Just let him come home
once more licking his lips at the thought of the fine,
rich, thick, hot, fragrant, dried salmon soup that is
waiting for him!"

"Just let him!" her outraged daughter agreed. "But how can we trick the trickster?"

"Trickster?" Her mother's eyes went wide at the word. "My dear, that handsome young scoundrel of ours may be Raven."

The two angry women went to work, gathering up every last scrap of food in the house. They piled it into their canoe. And by the time the sounds of the stone axe had stopped for the day, they were on their way to their old tribal village. "Any man will look good after that one," the widow snorted.

As they were paddling away, Raven was making his way homeward. And thinking of the lovely hot soup waiting for him at the hut, he whistled whenever he was not licking his lips.

But there was no smoke rising from the hut.

There were no women calling cheerily to him.

Worst of all, there was no food waiting for him. Not even cold food. Not even a bit of fat to chew. The hut was completely cleaned out.

Raven scowled. Then he shrugged. He had known it could not last forever. He had lived well for a while. And he had kept his promise. He had given the women a real surprise.

Chuckling a little at his own cleverness, Raven resumed his traveling.

As he grew only too well known in the villages, Raven had to go farther and farther afield to cope with his endless craving for food. And so it was that he found himself one day on a lonely plain.

It was a wide plain with only one house on it. There were no trees anywhere, only grass and flowers and the lone, large, carved house of a great chief.

He saw no one around the house. Yet there were sparks rising from the smoke hole. And there were voices singing. They were singing songs without words.

"Aha!" Raven said to himself. "Where there are sparks and singing, there is also good food." So he hid his feather cloak in some tall grass and walked on toward the large, lone house.

Still no one appeared. Still there was only the grass and the flowers and the mysterious singing.

Then he heard a voice call out. "A stranger is coming! A chief is coming!"

He knew they meant him. Yet how could they see him? There was no one anywhere around the house. Even when he reached the portal crestpole, no one appeared, anywhere. It was very unnerving.

Only his craving for food made him slip in through the opening in the carved portal pole.

There was no one inside the house, either. Yet he

still heard the voices singing. He saw the fire blazing in the center of the great gloomy house. And a fresh cedar mat had been laid out beside it.

"Sit down on the mat," the voice invited.

"On the mat. On the mat," the invisible singers echoed.

Raven hesitated, staying close to the doorway.

"This way, great chief!" the voice enticed him; and it seemed to move away from him toward the fresh mat. "This way, great chief! This way!"

"This way! This way!" the singers echoed.

Afraid, but also aware of what was expected of a "great chief," Raven walked proudly toward the mat. And he sat down gracefully on it.

"This must be the house of Chief Echo," he told himself.

As though hearing his thoughts, an invisible chief ordered his slaves to roast a dried salmon for his guest.

Raven's mouth was almost too dry to water as he watched a carved box open itself to let a dried salmon rise out of it and go to the fire to roast itself. His eyes were wide with more than wonder as he watched a carved wooden dish move to the fire, all by itself, to receive the hot fragrant salmon. And they shone with sheer gluttony as invisible hands cut the fish and laid it down before him.

Somehow, he controlled himself and ate calmly, as a chief eats.

Then a horn dipper offered him fresh water.

And then, while greed glittered more and more brightly in his eyes, a large dish of crabapples mixed with grease and a beautifully carved black horn spoon came to him, seemingly by themselves.

Even before he had finished the crabapples, his eyes were ranging the walls. They were devouring the mountain goat fat hanging there, and the mountain sheep fat, and—

The sudden laughter of invisible women startled him.

"Ha, ha," a woman's voice said. "Raven is thinking of snatching some goat fat and sheep fat and running away with it."

"Away with it. Away with it," the singers echoed; and their voices seemed full of teasing.

It was very unnerving.

Although they were invisible to him, even his thoughts were visible to them.

"I'm leaving," he decided there and then. But he simply could not make himself leave without a few pieces of rich mountain goat fat and luscious mountain sheep fat. So he leaped up, ran around the wall, snatched fat here and there as he dashed by, and raced straight to the exit.

Just as he reached it, a large stone hammer struck him on the right ankle. He fell, shrieking with pain.

Then invisible men dragged him out of the house.

So there he was, out on the plain again, empty-handed. He was alone again, and there were no trees anywhere. There was only the grass and the flowers and the large, lone, carved house with its singing voices and its sparks rising from the smoke hole.

An awful fear haunted him as he hobbled painfully toward the spot where he had hidden his flying blanket. What if invisible eyes had watched him hide it? What if invisible hands had taken it? Even burned it!

It was still there. Exactly as he had left it. And Raven lost no time becoming airborne.

But where could he go? Where could he go, now that people were becoming so terribly unfriendly?

Raven was beginning to lose his taste for travel.

As he was forced farther and farther afield, Raven came upon more and more of the strange beings who haunted the edges of the world then, in those days of very long ago when things were very, very different.

He was still limping badly from the hammer blow on his ankle on the evening he chanced upon a house standing by itself in the woods, close to the ocean.

"Aha!" he said to himself. "Lonely people are always kind to a poor, injured traveler." So as he approached the house, he limped far worse than he needed to. And as he expected, the man of the house bustled out to help him, while the pretty young woman of the house added more bits of fish to the fine thick soup she was making.

As soon as she had fed him, she put healing pitch on his ankle. And the power in the pitch should have

alerted Raven to the fact that these folk were supernatural. For it healed his ankle so fast and so completely that he found it hard to keep on limping.

But not too hard. For this was a very well provisioned house. And Raven had no intention of traveling on until it was not nearly so well provisioned.
In fact, as his eyes kept ranging greedily over the
stores of dried halibut and berry cakes and tasty oolachan grease and the pretty young woman who was to
serve them, he began to have more in mind than simply staying. His crafty old mind began to tell him,
"If *three* have to share the food, it isn't going to last
nearly as long as if only *two* have to share it."

He had to get rid of the man of the house, whose
name was Little Pitch.

The easiest way, Raven decided, would be to
drown him.

"You must let me go halibut fishing with you tomorrow," he said one evening, as he watched Little
Pitch ready his lines. "You must let me help to re-
place some of the food I have eaten."

"Well . . ." Little Pitch answered.

"Don't worry about my ankle!" Raven begged
him.

"It's . . . not that," Little Pitch admitted. "It's
just that . . . well. I have to fish at night. The . . .
the sun makes me weak."

"Indeed?" Raven said, with great interest.

"Uh . . . yes. The sun makes me weak. So I

always have to get back to the shade of the woods before the chill is off the morning."

"No problem," Raven assured him. "I'll be glad to fish by moonlight."

"Well. . . ."

"Just take me!" Raven coaxed. "Just let me repay my debt! And I'll do anything you say, sir. Anything!"

"Very well," Little Pitch agreed. And he let Raven paddle off with him to the halibut bank.

Little Pitch was a superb fisherman. He landed one great fish after another. But Raven was not so lucky. Somehow, he did not catch one fish.

"We'll have to go back now," Little Pitch told him when day was breaking.

"With my debt unpaid?" Raven implored him; and he did seem to be shamed. "Just a few more minutes, sir? I know what. You lie down in the shade of the bow there, and I'll cover you with a mat. I'll keep the mat wet, too."

"Well . . ." Little Pitch said.

"I'll look after you, sir," Raven assured him.

And the kind-hearted fellow, judging others by himself, agreed to a few more minutes.

Pretending great concern for his friend, Raven took plenty of time making Little Pitch comfortable in the bow; he took plenty of time covering him with a mat, and then dampening the mat.

Then he took plenty of time not baiting his hooks.

"Little Pitch?" he asked, with seeming concern for his friend.

"Hey!" Little Pitch answered, to reassure the good, kind stranger who only wanted to repay his debt.

Raven made noises as though splashing water on the mat, and then other noises, as though fishing.

By and by, he called again, "Little Pitch?"

"Hey!" Little Pitch answered; and this time his voice was weaker.

"Aha!" Raven said to himself. And he winked at the sun.

By and by, he called again, "Little Pitch?"

"Hey . . . Hey." The voice was very weak now.

"I have plenty of fish now," Raven lied. "So I will paddle home. As fast as a whale."

Paddling lazily back in the growing heat of the sun, he kept calling out, "Little Pitch?"

Little Pitch kept answering, "Hey!" in a voice that grew weaker and weaker.

Finally, there was no answer from under the mat.

So Raven lifted it to see what had happened.

Little Pitch had melted and run out over the halibut, making them black on one side.

With his purpose accomplished without even having to drown his good, kind friend, Raven soaked all the mats to keep the halibut fresh. Licking his lips at the thought of all the good dinners the pretty young woman would be able to cook for just him, he paddled faster and faster toward the lonely little house in the woods, beside the ocean.

He beached the canoe. And, too ravenous to unload it before eating, he hurried along the path toward the house.

But the house had vanished.

Worse still, its great supply of food had vanished with it.

Raven searched everywhere. But the house was gone. And where it should have been, a pretty little spruce tree was standing, with a drop of pitch on one side.

He was stunned.

At least, he had a canoeful of halibut. So he raced back to the beach.

But the canoe had vanished as completely as the house. And where it should have been, there was only a drift log—a fresh drift log with its pitch still on it.

"Well!" he said, outraged by the trick the supernatural couple had played on him. "A fine way to treat a poor, injured traveler!"

Then, with a shrug, Raven put on his feather cloak and resumed his traveling.

Even though the fishing trick had failed in the case of Little Pitch, Raven saw it as a face-saving way to serve his appetite. And as he became more and more a slave to his demanding master, he played the fishing trick in a variety of crafty versions.

The cleverness of the trick became all important. For his own craftiness was Raven's only possible source of pride now. Living as he did in a world of highly skilled animals and proudly skilled people, he had to get his food so skillfully that it satisfied *him* as well as Master Belly. A nobly born member of an aristocratic society had to be proud of himself.

Since he was now haunting the lonely edges of the world, the people he had to outwit were often strange beings who were sometimes an animal, sometimes a human, and always a challenge to his skill as a trickster.

One of these was Grizzly Bear, a changeable fellow who lived with his two changeable wives in a remote house by the sea.

Raven presented himself to them as a poor, injured traveler. Again he was kindly treated by people who seemed to be ordinary people. And again he insisted on helping with the halibut fishing to repay the kindness. But he was careful not to make the offer until he had everything set up for a clever trick, a trick he could really take pride in.

From the moment of his arrival at the remote house, it was clear to him that Grizzly Bear was a superb halibut fisherman. The house was so full of dried halibut that Raven could hardly bear to just sit there by the hour talking, talking, talking. But his plan demanded talk. Talk about halibut bait.

"Of course you bait with octopus," he said, pointing to the evidence of Grizzly Bear's success on the halibut bank. For everyone knew that octopus was the most enticing bait to that great, deep-sea fish.

"Of course," Grizzly Bear agreed. Standing on a certain rock as the tide ebbed, he told Raven, he always waited until the murk of the octopus den was visible at the bottom of the rock. Peering down through the water, he always watched until one of the dark, boneless shapes slithered out of its den. Then he stabbed. And with his long-handled devilfish-catcher, he pulled up a limp blob with eight long limp arms trailing.

"Unfortunately," Raven remarked, "an octopus is not always a limp blob. And his eight arms are not always trailing." Then he bit his lip, as if he really should not have said that to an octopus catcher. But Grizzly Bear glanced at him so alertly that, of course, he had to say more. "Oh, I'm sure you have never seen a bigger, darker shape looming out there, well off your rock," Raven said. And he swept his hand as if to dismiss the whole thing.

"A bigger, darker shape," Grizzly Bear echoed. "N . . . no." But he did not look any too sure that he never would see a bigger, darker shape looming out there, well off his rock.

"Good! I'm sure you never will," Raven boomed out, much too heartily.

So of course Grizzly Bear was even more anxious. "Have other men seen something looming out there?"

"Well. . . ." Raven was clearly reluctant to terrorize his good kind friend with all the tales he had heard from other halibut fishermen along the coast. "Yet. . . ." Who should be warned of danger if not a good kind friend? So, full of noble concern for his host, Raven told him fantastic lies about one fisherman after another who had encountered the Giant Devilfish, the Great Supernatural Octopus who was now ravaging the coast, wreaking vengeance on the men who captured devilfish to use as bait for their halibut fishing. His giant arms had crushed a killer whale, Raven said, terrifying a whole fleet of fishermen away from their halibut bank. Worse still, the Great Supernatural Octopus had wound his horrible sucking arms around the biggest of the fleeing canoes. And he had crushed it, too, as easily as a man would crush a kelp bulb.

Grizzly Bear listened, eyes wide and mouth wider. And as he heard tale after tale after tale, he began to shrink back from the octopus bait he had readied for his next day's fishing. "What am I going to do?" he wailed to Raven.

"Well. . . ." Raven was most reluctant to suggest what he *might* do. "I . . . I suppose you could give up halibut fishing," he hedged.

"Give up halibut fishing!" The dismay in his voice

assured Raven that halibut fishing was not only Grizzly Bear's source of food, but his source of pride also.

So Raven went craftily on with his plan. "Actually, there is something else you could do. . . . But no! Why should you do what the other halibut fishermen are afraid to do?" And he swept his hand again, as if to dismiss the whole thing.

Grizzly Bear swallowed. "Uh . . . what is it the other fishermen are afraid to do?" he asked Raven.

"Well. . . ." Raven was most reluctant to tell him.

"Tell me!" Grizzly Bear demanded.

"Well . . . if you insist."

Of course Grizzly Bear insisted.

"Well then . . . what all the fishermen say is that—"

"Tell me!"

"Well . . . if you really do insist. They say there is only one thing that will appease the Giant Devilfish. They say that if some very brave fisherman would bait his halibut hook with a piece of his own flesh, then the Great Supernatural Octopus would be appeased and would go away. . . . But no! Why should I even tell you? When not one of the other halibut fishermen is brave enough to try it."

"Not one," Grizzly Bear echoed. And his voice was dismal.

"Not one. Even though it would not be fatal. And even though they know that the man brave enough to go out there and do it would be admired up and down the coast. His name would ring forever in all the feasthouses. People would call him head chief of all the halibut fishermen in the world."

"Head chief of all the halibut fishermen in the world!" Grizzly Bear echoed. And now there was a hint of desire in his whispered words.

"They would tell of his deed at every potlatch," Raven went on. "But no, no, no, no. Not you, Grizzly Bear!"

"Why not me?" Grizzly Bear asked, now that Raven had put the thought into his head.

"Well . . . but yes! Why not you?" Raven answered, as if startled that Grizzly Bear had put the thought into his head. "Why not you, the greatest halibut fisherman on the coast?" He swept his hand grandly toward the great racks of dried halibut all about them. "Why not you?"

"Yes . . . why . . . not . . . me?" Grizzly Bear agreed, none too heartily.

"On one condition!" Raven said grandly. "You must let me go with you. How else can I ever repay your kindness? How else can I ever repay you for so much lovely, fragrant food?" Raven's insatiable appetite was gnawing at him. His eyes were devouring the lovely dried fish and dried berries all around him. His hands were itching to hurl Grizzly Bear out of the house at once, and gorge himself on food, food, food. But he controlled himself. He had to do this thing in a way he could be proud of.

"Bait from my own body?" Grizzly Bear mumbled.

"Bait from your own body!" Raven picked the words up with loud enthusiasm. "How that will ring in the feasthouse!" And he let out a wild twisting and turning of words that never let poor Grizzly Bear off the hook for a moment.

"Bait from my own belly?" Grizzly Bear mumbled again, later; and Raven caught protest in the mumble.

So he made one final twist into Grizzly Bear's pride. "Perhaps you had better let *me* do it. That's it. *I'll* do it. Alone!" His voice rang with pride.

"Oh, I'll do it," Grizzly Bear said, committing himself. But he did shake his head several times, later, and mumble as if he were having second thoughts about it.

When he had gone to bed, firmly committed to Raven's plan, that crafty fellow slipped out of the house. He made straight for a creek, where he caught a small salmon, cut off a piece of its flesh, and slipped back into the house with it, very pleased with himself.

Next morning, Grizzly Bear looked none too happy about the fishing trip. But he was committed. His pride was at stake. And Raven craftily carried him off on another wild flow of words.

All the way to the halibut bank, Raven kept peer-

ing through the water. And clearly his eyes were keener than Grizzly Bear's. For he kept seeing a big, dark shape looming. In fact, he saw the lurking Giant Devilfish so often that, by the time they reached the fishing grounds, Grizzly Bear looked none too ready for the deed that was going to ring in the feasthouses, down through the ages. He looked ready to rush home.

"I'll do the deed!" Raven proclaimed grandly, flashing his mussel-shell fishing knife. "And the only way to get human bait is fast," he said, seeming to slash at his own belly. Then, with the gasp of a valiant man, he triumphantly waved a piece of salmon flesh, keeping it well downwind from Grizzly Bear's keen nose. "I'll be called head chief of all the halibut fishermen in the world!" he gloated, reaching for a hook to bait.

"No, no, no!" Grizzly Bear cried out as he saw the great honor slipping away from him. He picked up his razor-sharp mussel-shell fishknife, moved it hesitantly near his belly. "The only way to get human bait is fast," he echoed. And, with a fierce spurt of resolve, he slashed into himself.

"What a thing to do!" Raven gasped.

Too late, Grizzly Bear caught Raven's triumphant grin and made an angry lunge at the trickster.

Raven just grinned again, jumped lightly overboard, and hung on to the bottom of the canoe until his groaning friend was faint enough to handle. Then he paddled him back to the house slowly enough to give him plenty of time to be nearly dead before they got there.

The two wives were easier to handle. Wild with grief at their loss, yet consoled by the glory that would cling to their husband's name, and also impressed by Raven's pretended grief, they were readily persuaded that they might bring their poor, dear, dying fisherman back to life by swallowing hot pebbles.

Raven was astonished but delighted—to see that as his three victims died, they took on grizzly bear forms. Now he could eat them as well as their wealth of provisions.

It was indeed a trick he could be proud of.

Raven visited many remote houses along the coast. And often his tricks fed his pride as well as his tyrannical Master Belly. But more and more often, he left the house muttering, "What a way to treat a guest!"

He was still haunting the edges of the world. He was still lonely and hungry, when he left the seacoast and flew inland.

Here the strange, edge-of-the-world people were land-hunters and rivermen.

The first house he chanced upon was richly carved with Wolf totems.

"Not the house of Chief Wolf!" he protested to himself. For a chief who was sometimes a man and sometimes a wolf would be sure to have eyes too sharp for Raven's liking.

Yet Chief Wolf was sure to be a superb hunter. In fact, thinking of all the deer meat there must be in that house, and all the mountain goat fat, and all the ducks and geese hanging up, Raven began to lick his lips. His mouth began to water. And when he could no longer stand the thought of all that luscious, juicy, fragrant food waiting in that house, he tore off his tattered flying cloak to approach it as an ordinary man.

By this time, he was so gnawingly, grindingly, groaningly empty that he had no trouble at all pretending to be a starving hunter who had lost his hunting gear as well as his way.

Chief Wolf was as warmly welcoming as all the other chiefs had been. And Raven had been right, for there were many fish roasting by the fire and a great deal of meat boiling, while on all sides were piles of fresh and dried food, ready for cooking.

Raven would have been blissfully happy if only the chief and all his people had not had such alert, slanted eyes and such quick, busy noses. How could he ever trick people like that? And when they smiled at him, their teeth were much too long for his liking.

He greedily gobbled up the roasted salmon they gave him first. Since they thought him a starving hunter, it was safe to show that he was as ravenous as he was. And besides, the wolf people ate their own food very fast. In fact, as he gobbled up the boiled dried meat that came next, and then the steamed fresh meat that came after that, and then the luscious, tart, frothy, pink, whipped soapberries that came after that, he wondered if it might not be a good thing to throw in his lot with Chief Wolf's people permanently.

Chief Wolf was very kind. When he noticed how ravenous his guest was, he turned to his hunters and said, "Go out early tomorrow and bring in fresh meat for our guest."

With all this encouragement, Raven ate so much that he wasn't hungry again until the house had hushed itself for the night. But then, when he started to rise from his sleeping robe to get a little snack, he sensed the alert lifting of heads all over the house. He heard the quick *sniff sniff* of a dozen noses.

"Pwtt!" he said to himself. "Wolf people never really go to sleep. They stay alert all the time. The scoundrels!" How was he ever going to be able to eat whenever he felt like it, as he would certainly want to do if he were going to stay on with them?

He was desperately hungry by the time he saw the young hunters slip out at dawn. And he licked his lips all day long as he watched them come back, two by two, with mountain goat, or venison, or black bear meat, or geese, or grouse. . . .

There was simply no end to the food!

Only no matter how gnawingly, grindingly, groaningly empty he was, he had to wait until the food was offered to him. And, of course, it wasn't offered to him nearly often enough.

Raven decided that he could never stand the strain of keeping his hands off so much tempting food day after day after day. So one morning he announced that he was off to search for his lost hunting gear. He was leaving his good, kind benefactors. But as he took one long, lingering, last look at Chief Wolf's provisions, he could not help adding, "I'll be back."

The chief ordered his slaves to prepare good fat meat for their guest to eat on his way. And he suggested directions.

"That way is the house of Chief Grouse," he told Raven. "We find him not too friendly. We like the grouse people, of course; but somehow they don't seem to like us." His eyes twinkled.

The grouse people rather appealed to Raven, since they were unlikely to be as alert as the wolf people, and their teeth might not be so alarming. So he circled round a bit and then headed for the house of Chief Grouse.

Here, again, he found a warm welcome. And the house seemed to be almost as lavishly provisioned as Chief Wolf's house.

Yet Chief Grouse did not send out bands of young hunters. He went out alone, with just slaves to carry the meat back home.

And such mountains of meat!

How did one man get so many mountain sheep? So many black bears?

Being tricky himself, Raven sensed a trick here. So he stealthily followed the chief one day when he went hunting. And when Chief Grouse stopped at the foot of a towering cliff, Raven stopped too. Peering through some concealing brush, he saw the chief raise his arms high before he began to shoot his arrows. To his amazement, the chief did not shoot at game. He shot at a crack in the cliff. And when he had sent all his arrows into the crack, he shouted four times. "Hey! Hey! Hey! Hey!"

Suddenly, there was a shining youth standing with Chief Grouse.

Raven gasped. Then his shoulders sagged. Once, a long, long, long time ago, he had been a shining youth.

"Whose arrows are those?" the radiant young man asked Chief Grouse.

Raven heard the young man's words distinctly. But he couldn't hear the answer as well. He couldn't quite make out the words when Chief Grouse answered, "O, dearest, supernatural helper! All these are your arrows."

The shining youth vanished. Raven blinked, to be sure. Yes! The shining youth had vanished.

Moments later, a mountain goat tumbled off the top of the cliff. Then another. And another. And yet another!

"What a way to get food!" Raven muttered in awe. And his eyes glittered greedily all the way back to the house.

He pretended to be astonished at how much food the chief brought back. "You are the greatest hunter in the world!" he said; and he made his voice ring with admiration. "Are you going hunting again to-morrow?"

"Not tomorrow," the chief answered. And a sweep of his hand over the four carcasses suggested that there was plenty of meat for tomorrow, so there was no need to go hunting.

"Then . . . perhaps . . . I could go hunting?" Raven suggested. "If you would lend me some gear. For I would like to provide myself with food and be on my way." He looked so concerned for his own pride that Chief Grouse gave him the bow and arrows at once.

Raven could hardly sleep. At last! he thought. At long, long last he had discovered a way to have all the food he wanted with almost no effort at all. He was up at dawn, away with his borrowed bow and arrows.

He made straight for the base of the towering cliff, where the wonderful thing had happened. And he, too, raised his arms high before he sent every arrow singing right into the crack. Then he shouted four times. "Hey! Hey! Hey! Hey!"

And there was the shining youth. Standing there beside him. Just as he had expected.

"Whose arrows are those?" he asked Raven.

"Uh . . ." If only he had been better able to hear what Chief Grouse had answered! Still, he was sure the chief had merely identified his arrows. "O, dearest supernatural helper!" Raven said. "All those are MY arrows."

The shining youth narrowed his eyes in anger. "Liar!" he called Raven, before he vanished.

Raven was so used to this compliment to his craftiness that it did not dash his high hopes. He looked expectantly up at the cliff. And something fell down.

But it was the arrows. Just the arrows. And every one was broken.

Raven sagged with despair. He was gnawingly, grindingly, groaningly hungry.

"Master Belly!" he shrieked. "You are the cause of all my troubles. Once I was a shining young prince, too, before you became my master. Well! Master Belly! Here is the food you deserve." And he plunged his hunting knife into his belly. Then he dropped to the ground, and lay there as though dead.

Later, Chief Grouse found him and left him for dead.

But Raven was immortal. He could not die.

When he finally stirred, his belly was more gnawingly, grindingly, groaningly empty than it had ever been before. And now it pained him, too, so much that he could barely stagger.

"I'll go back to Chief Wolf," he decided, "and tell

him Chief Grouse did this to me."

But it was a long, long way back for a man who actually had become the poor, starving, injured traveler he often had pretended to be. He had to keep resting as he went along.

He had had nothing to eat for four days when he woke up one morning to see a little tomtit fluttering anxiously around him.

"Please show me the way to Chief Wolf's house," he begged the bird. "But don't fly fast or zigzag! I'm very weak and my body feels heavy."

At the bird's inquiring glances, he explained what had happened. "I'd been hunting for days with Chief Grouse," he lied. "And every day I killed many mountain goats, while he couldn't kill one. He got so angry that he struck me with his club. He slashed my belly and threw me down a cliff."

The trusting little tomtit led the way to Chief Wolf's house, flying in short, straight, easy hops. And he did not leave Raven until he could see the smoke from Wolf House rising beyond the trees.

When Raven staggered into the richly carved house, everyone turned alert noses toward him. And there was a sound of sniffing.

"Your body is filled with blood," the chief said. "What happened?"

"Oh . . . I went searching for my hunting gear as I told you," Raven lied. "And I met a man who asked me to go hunting with him. So I went. But when I killed more mountain sheep than he did, and more black bears, he was so angry that he hit me with his club, slashed my belly, and threw me over a cliff. . . . I must have lain there, near death, for a long time. But when I finally came to, I remembered how kind you had been to me. So I staggered here to see you again before I die."

The chief vowed vengeance on the cruel hunter. And in the meantime, he urged his poor, wronged friend to try to get back his strength.

His slaves plied Raven with food. And to everyone's astonishment—except Raven's—he began to regain his strength. Soon he even felt well enough, he said, to go out with the young hunters.

"Well . . ." the chief countered. "You can go out with them, of course, but you may not be able to keep up. My hunters run as fast as birds fly."

"Well . . ." Raven answered. "At least I can go part of the way."

Actually, this suited him very well. For it made it easy for him to just sit lazily at the foot of a mountain while the young hunters raced up it, killed many mountain sheep, and then threw the carcasses down from a high cliff to where Raven waited.

"Aha!" he told himself. "Here's your chance to have a few tasty snacks hidden away for those hungry moments when nobody offers you any food." And he promptly covered some of the sheep with hemlock branches.

When the young hunters came down, they counted the carcasses, shook their heads, then sniffed around until they found the sheep Raven had covered with hemlock branches.

"Who did this?" the hunting chief asked, glaring straight at Raven.

"Oh, I did," he proudly claimed. "You were so long coming I was afraid that someone might stumble on those sheep over there and run off with them."

The hunting chief eyed him suspiciously. Then he threw back his head and howled the long-drawn-out, chilling howl of a wolf. "ow-oo-oo-oo-oo-oo-oo-oo-oo-oo-oo!"

Tribesmen and slaves came running, in answer to the call. They tied the carcasses to poles and carried them to Wolf House.

When Raven walked into the richly carved house this time, he sensed a new coldness in Chief Wolf— such a coldness that he did not suggest that he go out again with the hunters.

Instead, he stealthily followed them to the mountain. And this time, he did not try to hide any of the sheep with hemlock branches. Instead, he dragged a few well away from the others and stood over them with a borrowed bow, as if he had killed them.

But those horribly keen noses of the young hunters followed the scent back and forth. The sheep were dragged back to where they belonged. And this time, the hunting chief glared at him so hard, and gave such

a long-drawn-out, chilling wolf howl to call up the packers, that Raven hastily put on his tattered old flying garment.

By the time the packers ran in, he was on his way, traveling by air.

"I couldn't possibly stay with such suspicious people," he told himself. "Always glancing about. Always sniffing about. I could never be happy with them."

Wolf House would simply have to get along without him.

Yet, he was very, very weary of traveling.

For ages, word of Raven's tricks raced up and down the sea coast, up and down the rivers, from village to village. Every canoe carried yet another tale of the traveling trickster. Every feasthouse rocked with laughter, touched with dismay.

Then, suddenly, there were no new tales to tell, no new tricks to laugh about.

Raven had vanished.

"Perhaps," people suggested, "perhaps he found so much food somewhere, and ate so much, that he finally burst."

"Or perhaps he outraged one chief too many and had his traveling cloak torn to tatters," others guessed.

Gradually, though, most people began to believe that Raven wasn't traveling any more and tricking people any longer because he had been turned into stone. Someone had discovered a coastal rock that did look remarkably like a big raven; and all about it were other big dark rocks that looked terrifyingly like the old sea monsters mentioned in the tribal tales. And because people had a reluctant fondness for Raven, they spread one particular rumor about the rocks:

Raven, repenting of his misdeeds, had invited all the sea monsters to a potlatch. And somehow he had tricked them all into letting themselves be immortalized in stone. Only the Giant Devilfish, the Great Supernatural Octopus, had not been tricked, the rumor said.

That seemed likely, too, since there were still devilfish lurking in dens everywhere; yet there was something strange about them now—something that indicated a great fear of Raven. For, people noticed, if an octopus surfaced near them, all they had to do was *caw caw* like a raven; and the octopus vanished.

Generation after generation lived and died. And still the old tales kept circulating, with no new ones to tell. Still there was no word of Raven.

Then, suddenly, about a hundred years ago, a new rumor raced up and down the sea coast, up and down the rivers, from village to village.

Suddenly, this is what people were saying:

A young man was very fond of gambling. Every chance he got, he took his beautifully decorated gambling sticks out of their leather bag and played for high stakes.

For a time, he was so lucky that he won several magnificent Chilkat blankets as well as a pile of Hudson Bay blankets. He won three handsome canoes and a rifle.

Then his luck changed.

But, sure that the change was only temporary, the young man gambled more feverishly than ever.

"Stop gambling!" his wife begged him when his magnificent Chilkat blankets were gone, as well as his pile of Hudson Bay blankets.

"Not now!" he protested. "Not just when my luck is about to change."

"Please stop gambling!" she begged him when he had lost his last canoe on a wager.

"Not now!" he protested. "Not just when my luck is finally about to change."

"Please, please stop gambling!" she begged him when she saw him eyeing the carved chests that held their best belongings.

"Now?" he demanded, with a feverish brightness in his eyes. And he kept on gambling until everything in the chests was gone, until even the chests were gone too. Finally, he gambled away even his wife's clothes and his children's food. Only his rifle was left, and it was useless to him because he had gambled away all his bullets.

Now, desperate with shame, he rushed off into the hills. By following animal trails, he went far, far back into the mountains, farther than any man had ever gone before. And he took no notice of the way. For he wanted to banish himself forever.

For fifteen days he struggled on. And since he had no bullets for his rifle, he was almost dead from starvation as well as from fatigue, when he finally stumbled over one last mountain and saw a great valley below him. It was, he saw, a strangely lush valley, with steam rising in several places. But another glance told him that all he saw rising was not steam; some was smoke—the smoke of the one lone hut in the valley. And there was a narrow trail leading down the mountain to the hut.

The hut of the Wild Man of the Woods? he wondered. Alarmed at the thought of an ogre, he almost turned and fled. But craving food, the way he had once craved the excitement of gambling, he staggered down the trail. Staking his very life on chance, he approached the hut cautiously. And he peeked in fearfully.

A thundrous voice made him jump. "Come in!" the voice ordered. "For I have watched you struggling along the trail."

A huge man was sitting by the fire, stroking two tiny dogs—the kind of dogs that had never been seen since the long ago days of the old tribal stories.

"Come in!" the great voice thundered again.

The gambler swallowed. He hesitated near the doorway, for this was the biggest man he had ever seen, and the roughest looking. Then he noticed the mountains of meat by the fire. And his tongue began to lick his lips. His mouth began to water. His feet began to stumble toward the fragrance of the food, even though his mind told him that the food could be a trick to catch him.

"Why have you come here?" the giant of a man demanded.

"To . . . to banish myself."

"Do you know who I am?"

"N . . . no." Was he the Wild Man of the Woods? And if he was . . . ?"

"You have heard the old tales?"

"Y . . . yes," the young man admitted in a terrified whisper. So this was one of the monstrous beings that haunted those old tribal stories. But which one?

"You have heard of Raven?"

"Raven!" The gambler's voice brightened with hope. Raven did terrible things, of course, but only to get food when he was hungry; and this man was lavishly supplied with food. But Raven had lived in the days of very, very long ago. And anyway, he had been turned into a coastal rock. "You're not Raven," he said miserably. And his eyes slid back toward the meat. His tongue began to lick his lips again. His mouth began to water.

"I am Raven!" the great voice thundered. "Heaven banished me to the hills. I am Raven. But this time I'M not the starving traveler stumbling up to someone's house. You are. So eat!'"

Too hungry to care if it was a trick, the young man grabbed a chunk of warm meat. And for a time, there was no sound in the hut except the sound of eating, the sound of two men devouring food.

Even when the gambler was more than satisfied, his host went on eating . . . and eating . . . and eating . . . and eating. . . .

"You are Raven," the gambler said, convinced. "But why—?"

"Why am I not traveling? Why am I not playing magnificently clever tricks on people? Because . . ." His shoulders sagged. "Because heaven played an even more clever trick on me. Banishing me to this lush, warm valley. Surrounding me with deer and bear and sheep and goat. And giving me these superb hunters." He held up his two tiny dogs. "How can I leave?"

"Those . . . are your hunters?" They looked big enough to pull down a squirrel, or perhaps a rabbit if they really worked together.

"You don't believe the old stories?" He obviously meant the old stories about mythical little hunting dogs. According to the old tales, certain hunters had been given two magical dogs, Red and Spots, who were tiny when they were carried about, but who became huge and ferocious when they were put on the ground and then became tiny again when they were taken up and patted.

"When the dogs barked, the mountain goats fell

down from the mountains," the gambler whispered, recalling the old stories.

"You don't believe the old stories?" the giant of a man demanded.

"Well . . . uh . . . actually. . . ." Actually, since the coming of the white man, nobody had really believed any of the old tribal tales very much. Not even the tales of Raven. "Those dogs are very, very tiny," he respectfully pointed out.

"They're hauhau cubs," Raven claimed, furiously. And to prove that they were indeed those mythological beasts, he set them down with their heads toward the exit. "Get me a goat and a bear!" he ordered them.

The tiny creatures shook themselves. And as they bounded toward the opening, they grew bigger and bigger. Once they were outside, they became as big as two grizzly bears and twice as ferocious. They leaped off with a roar that seemed to shake the mountains.

The young man gasped. Things like that no longer happened in the world he knew.

He was still shaking when the incredible creatures came back with a goat and a bear. In fact, he didn't stop trembling until the hauhau cubs seemed to be tiny, gentle lapdogs once again.

"Now do you believe the old stories?" Raven challenged him.

"Y . . . yes. Yes, I do, Raven." He was really convinced by then. And he was also afraid.

Raven narrowed his eyes. "Do people still talk about Raven?" he demanded.

"Well . . ." the young man hedged.

"Do they tell of his magnificently clever tricks whenever they come together? Do they marvel at the prince of tricksters?"

"Well . . . sometimes . . . but—" The gambler moistened his lips to talk better. "But since the white man came, they talk more about . . . about other things."

"What other things?" Raven seemed outraged.

So, rather haltingly, the young man explained about ships and guns and trade blankets and money and forts and missionaries.

"They'll talk about me again when you go back," Raven predicted, with spirit.

"But—I'm not going back."

"Oh?" Raven challenged him. "You're not?" he said, setting the fabulous little dogs almost on the floor with their heads facing the guest and their eyes glittering at him.

The young man swallowed. "I . . . I could go back, I suppose," he said. But his eyes were very sad at the thought of the shame that awaited him in his village. "Uh . . . Raven . . . I . . . I would like to stay here forever."

"No, you wouldn't," Raven assured him. "Even though your forever wouldn't be nearly as long and lonely as my forever."

143

One more glance at the menacing little hauhau cubs convinced the young man that he really would not like it there. "Perhaps it would be better to go home," he agreed. "But I don't know the way."

"I do."

"You do? Then why don't you go back if you don't like staying here forever?"

"I told you. Because of heaven's magnificently clever trick. How can I leave this lush, warm valley to travel a hard, cold world? How can I leave all the luscious game? And how can I leave my fabulous little hunters? They might vanish forever if I went away. I can't leave. Yet . . ." He looked off toward the far mountains; and his eyes were filled with longing. "Perhaps . . . one of these days. . . ." He turned abruptly to the gambler. "Go back at once and tell the people about me. And tell them that Raven will be back, one of these days, with more fantastic tricks than ever. Tell them that he has nothing to do here except plan the tricks he'll play on them . . . tricks!" He seemed to fondle the word. "Life can get very dull without adventure," he told the gambler. "So what are you waiting for?"

"Well, I . . ." The young man wasn't actually finding life overly dull at the moment. He really did not feel the lack of adventure in his life.

"Skin the goat and bear! Take all the fat and meat you'll need for the journey and wrap them around this staff." He handed his guest a huge hunting staff beautifully carved with Raven totems. "You'll start back at dawn tomorrow."

"But—"

Raven stood with the hauhau cubs. And it did not take the gambler long to see that the odds were against him. "I'll start back at dawn tomorrow," he agreed.

"Take all the fat and meat you can carry," Raven invited him; and now his eyes glittered craftily. "Show people how generous Raven is to hungry travelers."

With Raven standing watch over the little dogs, who were also standing watch, the young man wrapped so much food around the big hunting staff that it was all he could do to carry it as well as his rifle. "I have a long way to go," he protested, as he set out.

"Not as long as you think," Raven told him, "if you follow my directions." And, leading the young man up the nearest mountain, he pointed a certain way. "Keep your eyes on the trail!" he ordered. "And if you hear anything behind you—like thunder or an earthquake—don't look back! And don't linger, for my dogs will soon be in the hills, hunting. Go fast! Stay on the trail! And don't look back until you have reached your village!"

The young man fled. And one roar from the watching dogs really sped him on his way. The trail led him soon to a flat plain where he ran, for terror seemed to lighten his burden. Then he began to hear terrible noises behind him: thunder, rockslides, earth-quakes, volcanoes. And he managed to go like light-ning.

Somehow, that very night, he was back in his village, with his food intact on the huge hunting staff. And he found the villagers trembling.

He looked back in terror. There were mountains where there had not been mountains before.

"I'm dreaming," he told himself. "I have been dreaming all along." But there was Raven's staff, with Raven's food around it.

The people gathered about him. They heard his story and were in a mood to believe it.

Later, of course, some people began again to have their doubts about Raven.

But others—especially the young people—went again and again into the hills to see if they could find Raven.

So far, no one has found him.

Yet, there are still people who turn fearful eyes on any huge black bird that comes along. "Who knows?" they ask other people.

THE PEOPLE
WHO OWNED
THE STORIES

The *Tlingit* tribes of Alaska.

The *Haida* of the Queen Charlotte and Prince of Wales Islands.

The *Tsimshian* of the British Columbia mainland, south of the Tlingit and east of the Haida.

The *Kwakiutl*, south of the Haida and the Tsimshian.

These were the native Indian linguistic groups who carved the unique totem poles of the Pacific Northwest. These were the storytellers who owned the tales their poles and their houses and their household goods illustrated.

The stories were owned. They were owned and cherished like the houses and the heraldic crests we

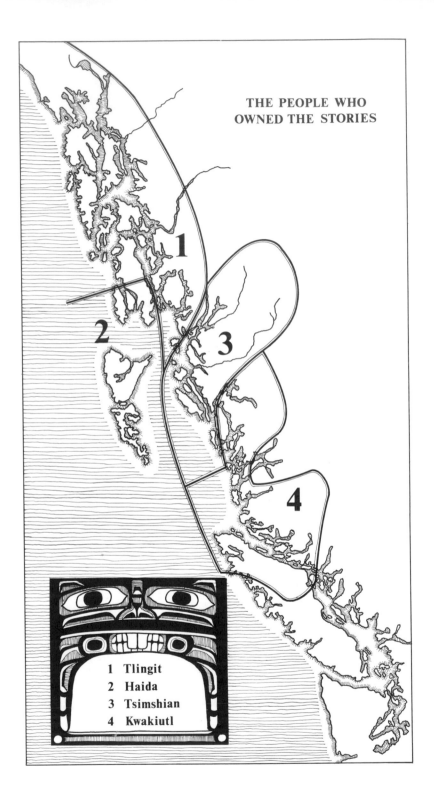

THE PEOPLE WHO
OWNED THE STORIES

1 Tlingit
2 Haida
3 Tsimshian
4 Kwakiutl

call *totems*. They were protected like the great cedar canoes and the hereditary fishing stations. Only a certain family could tell a particular version of *The Prince Who Was Taken Away by the Salmon* or of *Raven Traveling* at a potlatch. And the family's storyteller was handsomely paid for his colorful performance.

And who knows? The ghosts of those original owners may still be standing watch over the stories. They may be hovering around the modern storytellers who, in turn, develop and own their versions of the ancient tales. For hovering ghosts were certainly part of the way of life of these people.

GHOST
STORY

Once there was a lively little prince who craved adventure. But it was not the kind of adventure you might expect of an Indian boy in the wild, mountainous Northwest. He did not crave sea hunting or goat hunting in the hills. He did not even yearn to go out catching eagles. He wanted to do something much, much more exciting. He wanted to go adventuring where his body could not take him.

One day he told his four friends about it.

The five little Eagle-crest nobles were watching an eagle soar high above them when the prince blurted it out. "I'm going to move through the air, too," he told them. "And see the faraway world the way an eagle sees it."

"But Sea-Hawk!" his friends protested. "Nobody can move through the air."

"No body," he agreed. "So that's why I've got to get out of my body."

His friends were not as astonished as you might think. In those days of long ago, people were very much aware of their two selves: their body self that would die, and their spirit self that would live on forever. They were very much aware of the two worlds they lived in: the solid world of everyday things and everyday people, and the gossamer world of ghosts.

"I'm going to journey through the air," Sea-Hawk went on. "And I'm going to journey through the ocean and see that world too, the way a whale sees it."

"But Sea-Hawk!" his friends protested.

Only a shaman, a medicine man, learned how to get out of his body to make such fantastic spirit journeys.

"I'm going to be a shaman," the prince confided to his friends.

"But—" his friends protested again, because everyone knew that Sea-Hawk's family intended him to be the head chief his birth entitled him to be.

"I'm going to be a shaman. And you're going to help me," he told his comrades.

The very next day, the five boys slipped away from the village. And they kept on slipping away, day after day after day. To keep people from guessing what they were up to, they always took their bows and arrows or their balls and hooked sticks or their spears and hoops.

When they reached their secret place in the woods, they cached their sports equipment and started playing shaman.

It took a long time to build a secure little hut to keep their things in and to mark it with their identifying crests. It took a long time to make a crown of bird claws and a dancing apron that clattered with hazelnut shells. It took a long, long time to make four sets of regalia for the shaman's helpers, five medicine rattles, and decorated boards with sticks for beating time, and bone whistles. And it took an even longer time to create medicine songs and dances. But it was such fun that they all decided to become shamans, with Sea-Hawk the most important shaman, of course. And they talked endlessly about the adventures they would have, high in the air, deep in the ocean, and even over the misty bridge into the shivery Land of Ghosts.

The days flew by, and the moons, and the seasons. The years seemed to have wings. The boys grew older and bigger. Yet their ambition never changed. They were still going to be shamans.

Since their families did not know about the secret games, the five Eagles were trained and educated like other youths of their class. Nobles were expected to be stronger and more skillful and more graceful than common people. So they swam in the icy water every morning and then had their bodies whacked and rubbed with green boughs until their skin flamed like the sunrise. They learned to paddle and hunt and fish, to speak eloquently, and to perform the tribal ceremonies. They learned the art and the law, their own rights and their neighbors'.

Actually, they were glad of their training, for they knew that medicine men needed tough bodies, alert senses, and very sharp minds, as well as superb artistry in performance. They paid rapt attention to the storytellers and the singers and the dancers, especially when the performer was a professional doctor.

Yet they always found time for their secret rites in the woods. In fact, they were still so wrapped up in the old boyhood dream that it came as a shock when the chiefs began making arrangements for Sea-Hawk to take his destined place in society.

Suddenly, his relatives were readying the envoys who would go out to the distant villages, delivering the invitations to the potlatch, to the great feast at which Sea-Hawk would be installed in his proper place in the tribe. Suddenly, people were talking about the great name that would be his rightful hereditary title. They were talking about the famous crests that would be presented to him with the accompanying songs and stories and dances. Suddenly, there was no more time for dreaming wild dreams about fantastic spirit journeys.

Aghast at the fact that his family's plans for him

were already in motion, Sea-Hawk fled to the hideout in the woods, with his friends close behind him.

"It's now or never," he gasped. "I'll have to tell them. But what if they won't let me be a shaman?"

"Oh," his best friend countered, though none too confidently, "they'll let you be a shaman if you show them you have enough talent to be a good one." For everyone knew that shamans—those men and women in touch with the other world—were greatly respected in the villages. Sometimes they were even more honored than the head chief. Always they were more feared, more deferred to.

"Well," Sea-Hawk agreed, also none too confidently, "then maybe I'd better show them I have talent, IF I do have talent."

He meant a talent for touching the other world, for communicating with the ghosts and spirits who could do so much good or so much harm to people. Who could make them sick or well.

"There's only one way to find out," Sea-Hawk went on.

"And there's no time to lose," his best friend, Little Wolf, reminded him.

"There's no time to lose," Sea-Hawk agreed.

"It had better be impressive," Little Wolf urged.

"Yes, it had better be impressive," Sea-Hawk agreed, knowing that there was only one way to impress his family with his talent for touching the other world. And it was no way for a coward. With so little time to convince them of a true gift for medicine, he would have to touch the cold, clammy world of ghosts. And the only way into that world was through the graveyard.

"It's now or never," he said. And turning about, he darted off toward the burial ground, with his four friends close behind him.

The burial place was set well in back of the village, on the bank of a brook that flowed dark and silent through yielding moss and muskeg. To reach it, the boys had to skirt the village and then follow a trail that twisted through dark, drooping cedars and past firs that stood silent in the silence of a world hushed by deep, deep, green mosses. Pale owls flitted like ghosts among the trees; and like ghosts they made no sound in passing.

Newly alert to the dark brooding of the forest, the boys were almost as silent in their passing. And newly aware of the hovering presence of the ghosts of the dead, they emerged quietly into the openness of the graveyard.

Dusk was falling. The shadows of the trees were creeping out silently to shroud the grotesquely shaped and grotesquely fruited grave trees. For, slung up in the trees, were the painted coffins of the dead; and where ancient coffins had broken open, there was the glimmer of scattered bones under the trees. There were old, old skulls, green with moss and haunted with dark, empty eye sockets.

Unnerved by what he must do, Sea-Hawk slipped quickly toward the mortuary poles of the great chiefs. In the fading light, the carved Ravens and Bears and Eagles and Wolves and Killer Whales on the poles seemed to be waiting. He looked up at the great carved cedar plank that hid the totem-painted coffin of his dear old grandfather.

"You have the emblems of our family set like a fort around you," he whispered to his grandfather. "Our supernatural helpers will help me, too." There was power in the great totems. He could feel the power pulsing out into the silence of the graveyard.

Then he saw a new, empty Eagle coffin resting on a broad, low pole. He saw a white owl glide over it, silent as a disembodied spirit. He moved swiftly toward it, then turned to look at his four friends.

They swallowed their protests. Sea-Hawk must prove his talent for touching the cold, clammy world of ghosts.

Only a light mist wreathing through the grave trees and mortuary poles suggested the Land of Ghosts that lay just beyond them. Only a heavier drift of mist above the dark brook suggested the ghost bridge that spanned an invisible ghost river, giving the ghosts of the dead their way out of the Land of Ghosts into the graveyard where they still kept watch over the skeletons they had once used.

The sudden, eerie screech of an owl curdled the boys' blood.

Sea-Hawk swallowed. Then he laid a resolute hand on the empty coffin.

"But Sea-Hawk!" His friends could not help voicing one protest.

"The emblems of my family are set like a fort around me," he answered. And climbing into the coffin, he lay down. He lay utterly still and silent. Still and silent as death.

His four friends, really frightened now, looked at one another.

"We'll stay," Little Wolf announced. "Who knows what will happen?"

The others nodded in solemn agreement. They stood hushed with awe. For there were great forces surging silently in the world all about them. And with their fear-sharpened senses, they were more deeply aware of those forces than they had ever been before.

The world darkened. And nothing moved. Nothing but the eerie owls who glided over the graveyard, pale and silent as ghosts.

One lighted on the coffin and stared at them with large, round, yellow eyes fixed immovably in their sockets.

"I think I'd better go home," one of the boys whispered. "He's well off the ground. So the animals won't get at him." And he slipped away, along the trail to the village.

Little Wolf moved stealthily to look into the coffin. He caught his breath. "He's dead," he whispered.

Then he leaned closer. "No, his heart's beating," he reported. "But that's all," he said. And his eyes were wide with wonder. "Do you think his soul has already left his body?"

"I think maybe I'd better go home too," one of the other boys said. "What could we do if something did happen?" And he slipped away, along the trail to the village.

A little later, the third friend slipped away.

Only Little Wolf was left in the graveyard with the still, silent, empty husk of his best friend.

Where was Sea-Hawk? he wondered. Moving through the air, seeing the world as an eagle saw it? Or moving deep through the ocean, seeing that mysterious world as a whale saw it?

The moon rose, touching the grave trees and mortuary poles with ghostly silver and making the dark shadows darker than they were. A faint breeze stirred. And there were tiny, cautious rustlings.

Suddenly, Little Wolf shivered. He felt his hair rise on his neck. He felt his skin tighten and turn cold at the base of his spine. The ghosts had come over the bridge. The ghosts were moving into the graveyard.

An owl shrieked. And Little Wolf fled along the shadowy trail that twisted through dark, drooping cedars, past firs that stood silent in the silence of a world hushed by deep, deep, green mosses.

He burst into the house, darted toward the cheerful light of the fire, and felt a hand on his shoulder.

"Where is Sea-Hawk?" one of the prince's uncles demanded.

Little Wolf swallowed. Where *was* Sea-Hawk? He licked his dry lips. "He's . . . lying in a coffin in the burial ground."

The hand tightened on his shoulder. "Tell the chief!"

The boy moved reluctantly toward the waiting figure of the chief. And looking into those intent, observant eyes, he could tell nothing less than the whole truth.

"Great Tribe!" the chief said, turning toward the silent, waiting people, "We are going to the burial place to bring the prince home. Light your torches!"

The order raced from house to house in the village. And soon the tribe was moving in single file along the trail, their torches of pitchwood and maple bark and oolachan fish throwing fantastic shadows on the drooping cedars and on the firs that stood silent in a world hushed by deep, deep, green mosses.

In the burial ground, the torches made rings of flame to light the still, silent body of the prince, while men lifted it out of the coffin and laid it on a cedar plank covered with fresh mats. Then a low chant started as the flames moved slowly along the forest trail again, back toward the waiting village.

The shamans circled the prince with wild, frenzied dances before the men laid him close to the fire in the chief's house. And the stirring flames seemed to continue the spirit-dancing as they flickered over the watching faces of the people and reached into the gloomy corners to reveal the startling faces carved on the great cedar houseposts. Supernatural Eagles and Bears, too, seemed to be breathlessly waiting, to see what was going to happen to the prince who had dared the cold, clammy ghosts in the graveyard.

He had dared the ghosts without proper training in handling the wild, surging, invisible forces of the world. And now he seemed dead.

Yet his heart was beating faintly. His body self was still waiting for the return of his spirit self. But was that self lost? Was it unable to find its way back to its body? Would it stay lost until the heart stopped?

The people watched and wondered, their eyes on the frantic shamans. But the prince did not stir.

While it was still night, messengers slipped away to other villages to summon other shamans. They carried the chief's offer of a rich reward to the medicine man who could bring the prince's spirit self back to his body.

Excited by this challenge, all the shamans came at once. And for four days and four nights, they worked over the boy in turn. They crowned their long straggly hair with circles of grizzly-bear claws, and round their gaunt bodies they tied dancing aprons that clattered with puffin-bill fringes. They beat their medicine boards with wild rhythms and shook their medicine rattles. Framed against the gloom of the great cedar house by the red glow of the flames, they leaped and danced themselves into frenzies to activate deep, occult powers in themselves. Sometimes one would fall into a trance and lie as though dead while his spirit self went searching for the prince's. And one by one, they laid their most powerful carved bone charms on the youth's body.

They were all beating their boards near him when the prince opened his eyes.

At long last, his spirit self had come back to his body. And the wild joy of the tribe rang through the house, through the village. People laughed and wept and chanted as the shamans were rewarded for their great work.

For some time, the prince lay by the fire, still but alert, as though exhausted yet stimulated by some fantastic adventure. His four friends stood watch.

"Where were you?" they demanded.

"What happened?"

"Were you frightened?"

"Did you really move through the air?"

"Did you really see the world as an eagle sees it?"

"Did you see any ghosts?"

"What did you see, Sea-Hawk?"

"I saw . . ." The prince's eyes seemed to hold the almost-frightening brightness the boys had often glimpsed in medicine men's eyes. "I saw the spirit self of every man shimmering around his edges . . . men . . . trees . . . animals . . . flowers. . . .

Every living thing was edged with a misty glow."

"Even . . . us?" Little Wolf asked in an awed whisper.

"Even you, Little Wolf." Suddenly Sea-Hawk sat up and laughed at his friend's wide-eyed wonder. "Your spirit self has a very strong glow. And some day you'll make a spirit journey with me. Some day you'll see . . . what . . . I saw." His voice sank into an awed whisper. His eyes went wide with wonder. "There's nothing in our world like it, Little Wolf," he said. "I am going to be a shaman."

"If they let you," Little Wolf cautioned. For all through the dreadful days he had sensed that the chief still planned to have Sea-Hawk installed in his rightful, hereditary place in the tribe. It was what everyone had always expected. Changes were not easy in the tribal hierarchy. A noble's duty could not be simply tossed off.

Sea-Hawk was not listening. Caught up in what he

163

had seen on his fantastic spirit journey, he fingered the carved bone charms the shamans had piled on his body, then he hung them around his neck. And finally, as though the power in the charms was surging into him, he leaped up. He lifted his head fiercely. And his eyes blazed. "I will be a very great shaman," he predicted.

Little Wolf caught his breath. Then he shook his head to clear it. He blinked his eyes, twice. For he had glimpsed something. For one moment it had been as if Sea-Hawk were standing against the Northern Lights. But he must have been mistaken, he told himself. It must have been the firelight. Little Wolf shook his head again.

The chief was Sea-Hawk's uncle. And the chief's plans for his heir seemed to be going ahead exactly as before.

Then grief struck the village. Suddenly, without warning, the chant of sorrow swelled out from the second largest house in the village, the house with the Wolf totems. "AIE AIE AIE! He has left us! AIE AIE AIE!" Over and over it swelled. "AIE AIE AIE! He has left us!"

Sea-Hawk raced into Wolf House, with his friends close behind him. For it was the home of his father's Wolf clan family.

His father's sad eyes lighted at the sight of his son. "It is the old chief," he said.

"AIE AIE AIE! He has left us! AIE AIE AIE!"

"He had so wanted to see if you would manage to become a shaman," Sea-Hawk's father confided.

"He will not only see," the youth told his father. "He will join in the ceremonies. I will restore him to life."

"My son!" The father's eyes were intent on his son. "Can you do that?"

"I can do that."

Sea-Hawk fled to the secret place in the woods, with his friends in attendance.

"Our regalia is ready," he remarked, taking a crown of grizzly-bear claws out of a carved chest.

"For what?" Little Wolf asked.

"Yes. Ready for what?" the other friends demanded, as they lifted out the sacred charcoal and eagle down, the medicine rattle and the clattering dancing apron and the white tail of an eagle. Sea-Hawk couldn't really be about to do what he had promised.

Again, as Sea-Hawk looked at his friends, his eyes seemed to hold a wild, unearthly brightness. "I am going to bring the old chief back to life," he announced with quiet conviction.

There was no interfering with the prince's plans. He knew what he was going to do, and how he was going to do it. All he wanted from his friends was a spirited performance as shaman's helpers. "Don't worry about it!" he told them, "I'm not counting just on you. I have a supernatural helper now."

People caught their breath. Perhaps the prince could bring the old chief back to life. They hugged their blankets close and kept their gaze on his every movement. They swayed with him, and echoed his every owl hoot.

It was evening. Sparks leaped up toward the smoke hole, and out toward the dark sky as the shaman prince began to sing a strange song, a song filled with soft hoots and sudden screeches. Then he began to dance in a way that not even his close friends had ever seen him dance before. Each time he circled the fire he seemed to swoop silently down on the dead man. And whenever he held still, as if searching about him for direction, he swiveled his whole head as though his eyes had been fixed immovably in their sockets. And after his fourth circling of the fire, his swoop toward the dead man was accompanied by a blood-curdling shriek.

"It *is* the owl." Little Wolf's lips made the words, but his voice did not rise to say them.

When the shaman prince finally spoke, however, it was in his own voice. "The old chief is now in the village of the Ghosts," he said. "And my supernatural helper says that I shall bring his soul back to his body. . . . Fetch me a fragrant new cedar-bark blanket!" he commanded.

His four attendants glided away as if they too were possessed by owl spirits. And they handed him the wrap in silence.

168

Sea-Hawk exchanged his white eagle tail for the cloak. Then, speaking in a loud, carrying voice, he commanded everyone to stay in Wolf House until he came back.. They were to join his attendants, he said, in beating on the hollow cedar planks and on the skin drums. "And sing as loud as you can to coax the soul back!" he ordered.

He slipped out into the darkness of the night alone. Silent as an owl, he followed the trail that twisted through the dark drooping cedars, past the firs that stood silent in the silence of a world hushed by deep, dark green mosses. Pale owls flitted like ghosts among the trees; and, like ghosts, they made no sound in their passing.

Now, when Sea-Hawk reached the burial place, he could see the ghost bridge and the steaming, boiling ghost river that flowed under it without sound. He sat down at the edge of the gossamer world of ghosts. And a feeling of lightness came over him. The lightness rose in him, up, up, up out of his solid body. He felt himself float free of his solid body. He saw his body there, below him, while he, his spirit self, floated down to the gossamer bridge. He was there on the ghost bridge, all of him, looking much as he had looked before. But now he and his regalia and even his medicine rattle were made of some gossamer substance. He was paler than he had been and more luminous, yet not gray as the ghosts were gray. And he sensed that he was not cold, as the ghosts were cold—

the ghosts he could see moving in the village across the ghost river.

He glanced back at the trees and at the moss in the graveyard. And again he saw that living, vibrating radiance that edged them. The world was more gloriously alive than most people suspected.

But not across the river. A soft owl's hoot drew him back to his purpose. He went over the bridge. And there the coldness touched him, the coldness of ghosts.

He saw faces he knew among the ghosts; and he cautioned them to silence. "Conceal me!" his hands said. And he slipped into the biggest of the gossamer houses unobserved by the chief of the ghosts.

There he found the filmy form of the old chief who had just died, vaguely diffuse, unsure yet of his new surroundings. And an eagerness leaped up in the ghostly eyes at the sight of the youth.

Again, Sea-Hawk cautioned silence. "Come with me!" he beckoned to the old man.

Ghost relatives glided around them as they fled to the ghost bridge and crossed it.

And there at the edge of the ghost river of boiling oil, there at the edge of the graveyard, Sea-Hawk slipped back into his solid body. "Now I will take you back to your body," he told the new ghost.

At once, the ghost contracted. The filmy substance concentrated itself into a small glow of energy, which Sea-Hawk grasped in his left hand and held safe as he fled back along the trail to the village.

The drums were still beating. The people were still singing as the shaman prince leaped triumphantly into the great cedar house.

The drums stopped. The singing stopped too. Even breathing seemed suspended as the youth dropped his cloak from his shoulders and glided toward the dead man's body, with his left hand high. Eagle down drifted away from his crown of grizzly-bear claws, and the puffin-bill fringe of his dancing apron clattered in the hushed house as he circled the fire four times. Then he swooped down on the dead man, opening his left hand on the silent body. "Eagle tail!" he commanded; and at once it was in his hand to fan the first breath of the old chief.

The dead man sat up.

The people gasped. Then they burst out into joyous shouts.

"The prince *is* a shaman," Little Wolf whispered. "The prince is a very great shaman."

The chief could only agree. Even without any training from the tribal medicine men, the prince was a very great shaman. And since the honor of his young clansman was close to his own honor, the chief said, "We will give Sea-Hawk a great medicine name at the potlatch . . . and install Raven's Wing as my true heir." Raven's Wing was a younger nephew.

"They must give me a very great name," Sea-

Hawk insisted so forcibly that Little Wolf raised his eyebrows. Too much ambition was not good in a doctor.

But it was increasingly clear that Sea-Hawk was ambitious. It was as if he were determined to show that he could win more honor as a shaman than he could have won as head chief of a great tribe. Or as if the dream of being a medicine man had been dreamed so long that only exceptional success could make the reality as good as the dream had been. "Or," Little Wolf loyally suggested to his friends, "as if what he has already seen in the other world has excited him to push his powers to the limit. There is very great power in a very great name; so he wants it, to help him."

Others who were less fond of Sea-Hawk said that success had gone to his head.

Shamans, especially, glared at the boy who demanded a greater medicine name than any of them had. What infuriated them most was that he had accomplished his feat with their charms.

"If we had known you meant to be a shaman," they told him, "we would never have given you our most powerful charms when we brought you back to life."

"You did not bring me back to life," he corrected them. "For I had not died. My spirit self would have returned without your help."

"That may be true," Little Wolf pointed out to his

friend. "But you are using their most potent charms."

". . . better than they would use them," Sea-Hawk pointed out in turn.

Little Wolf shook his head sadly.

"Little Wolf!" Sea-Hawk protested. "It's all coming out just as we planned! I'll be the greatest shaman in the world, and you'll all be lesser shamans. It's exactly as we planned."

It wasn't exactly as Little Wolf had planned. Instead of adventuring out to see the world as an eagle saw it or as a whale saw it, the shaman prince seemed to go only to the ghosts' village. And instead of curing the sick, he seemed to be more and more caught up in spectacular feats of bringing the dead back to life. There was his father's niece, then a man in another village, then a chief's favorite wife.

Thinking about the niece and the man and the chief's wife, Little Wolf felt his hair rise. Those three dead brought back to life were not quite like other people. Neither was the old chief brought back to life. There was something spooky about them. Something a little chill and gray. Something that made others edge away from them. They were ghoulish.

He talked to Sea-Hawk. But the shaman prince did not listen. In fact, he seemed scarcely aware of his old friend. His strangely wild eyes seemed to be burning right through Little Wolf and seeing far beyond him.

As the shaman prince brought more and more dead people back to life, no tribal medicine name seemed great enough for so gifted a young man to have. He came to be called simply Shaman Prince. And people paid him so lavishly for his work of restoring loved relatives to life that he became wealthy.

Yet, when these relatives were restored to life, people were not as happy as they had thought they would be. Little Wolf was aghast at the unease in the village as an increasing number of vague, grayish people haunted the gloomy corners of the great cedar houses. He tried to reason with his old friend. But Shaman Prince seemed obsessed with his own power.

Meanwhile, the ghosts across the invisible bridge were becoming very angry. Every new ghost that came to live with them was being cleverly snatched away before it had time to settle into the new life. And even happily settled ghosts were slipping away over the bridge, and hovering around villages until they found bodies to slip into. Other ghosts, agitated over the emptying of the great gossamer houses, kept stumbling into, or backing into, the ghostly River of Boiling Oil, thereby dying their second death and going on to their next phase, as Salmon People. Houses echoed with emptiness.

Finally, the chief of the ghosts called a war council in Ghost Town.

"Next time Shaman Prince comes here, we will cut off the end of the bridge," the war council agreed.

"We will drop him into the River of Boiling Oil." That way, his spirit self would not linger in Ghost Town. Instead, it would be instantly routed on into the next phase. It would go to a Salmon Village to become the vital part of one of the Salmon People.

And to be sure that Shaman Prince would come again, soon, the war council sent a raiding party to his village that very night to snatch away a man's soul while he was sleeping.

In the morning, relatives found the man dead. And instead of chanting sadly as they would have done in the old days, instead of assuring one another that he was not really dead, but only gone to join other equally loving relatives in Ghost Town, everyone rushed to Shaman Prince. "He was not ready to die," they protested. "Bring him back to us, Shaman Prince!"

"He was not ready to die," Shaman Prince agreed. "The ghosts have taken him because they are plotting to kill me."

People gasped.

"Call the tribe together!" he commanded.

When the people were gathered, Shaman Prince commanded them to sing and sing and sing until he got back. "Sing all my songs!" he commanded. Then he glided away along the trail to the graveyard. And he was soon in Ghost Town.

This time, his ghost relatives edged away from him. But they made no move to stop him as he slipped into the chief of the ghosts' house and snatched up the soul of the newly dead man. In fact, it was only when he moved back toward the River of Boiling Oil, back toward the misty bridge with the man's soul, that the ghosts really seemed aware of their enemy's presence. Then they made a rush for him.

He leaped triumphantly onto the misty bridge, well ahead of his pursuers. And he was almost over it when it gave way beneath him. He made a frantic leap, landing so close to the bank of the real world that only his feet touched the ghost river. His gossamer body fell forward onto solid earth.

The soul escaping with him fell right into the river and disappeared in the boiling mists.

Groaning with pain, Shaman Prince pulled himself free of the river and re-entered his solid body. With superhuman resolve, he made himself run along the trail to the village. But before he reached the house where the people were still singing, he fell to the ground, groaning.

It was Little Wolf who sensed the groaning and slipped away from the singing, followed by his

three friends. And the four youths carried their prince into the house. They laid him down on a plank covered with fresh cedar-bark mats.

The house hushed itself, and people's hearts sank. The great Shaman Prince would die, and no one would even try to bring him back because he had already partly died his second death. His feet had been burned in the terrible River of Boiling Oil.

He did not seem to see the people who gathered anxiously around him, nor hear faithful Little Wolf. Looking through people and beyond them, he listened only to his supernatural helper.

"Get up!" his power told him. "Run around the fire! Following the course of the sun, run four times around the fire!"

People gasped as they saw the prince rise on his horribly burned feet. They watched, open-mouthed, as he ran around the fire four times. Then they drew back in awe as they saw that his feet were both healed.

"Now I have more power than ever!" Shaman Prince called out. "Now I can bring back people who have been dead for many days."

Though Little Wolf protested again and again, Shaman Prince became more and more wild-eyed, more and more straggle-haired, more and more determined to empty Ghost Town and fill the edges of the real world with increasingly ghoulish people. The stench of death began to blow through the village.

And across the river, the agitated ghosts were falling more and more often into the River of Boiling Oil, leaving the great gossamer houses more and more lonely.

Finally, the chief of the ghosts called another war council.

"We will give Shaman Prince a challenge he cannot resist," they agreed this time. "We'll say that the chief of the ghosts is sick and wishes the prince to save him from his second death."

By this time, Shaman Prince had so much power and so many supernatural helpers that he knew what the ghosts were planning. He even knew they intended to raid his village as soon as he had left it; they were going to snatch many souls of sleeping people to repopulate Ghost Town. So he called the tribe together and told them what would happen.

He also told them what to do. They were to mix certain poisons and evil-smelling things and sprinkle the mixture around the houses before they went to sleep. "Then, when the ghosts come in the night with their dried-nettle arrows, they will find that things happen differently than they expect."

At once, the people gathered the poisonous things and the evil-smelling things. But they did not sprinkle the mixture around the houses until two ghostly messengers had come for Shaman Prince in the night, and until he had gone off with them along the trail that twisted through dark, drooping cedars and past firs that stood silent in the silence of a world hushed by deep, deep, green mosses.

Confident of his own powers, the gossamer Shaman Prince went into the ghost chief's house. He calmly opened the filmy chest of ghost medicine regalia and took out the crown of dead-men's ribs. He shook out the dancing apron that clattered with a fringe of dead-men's bones. And he lifted up a rattle that was a skull, with a backbone for a handle.

Before he put on the crown of dead-men's ribs, though, he blew water into the hollow of his right hand and rubbed it on his forehead. Before he put on the apron that clattered with a fringe of dead-men's bones, he blew water into the hollow of his right hand again and rubbed it on his thighs. And before he shook the rattle that was a skull and backbone, he blew water yet again into the hollow of his right hand and rubbed it on both arms, while the supposedly sick chief of the ghosts scowled at him.

He was about to start work when he heard the hullabaloo outside. It was the raiding party, returned from the village.

"Our dried-nettle arrows failed us!" ghosts were complaining.

"Our arrows turned on us, killing some of us instead," ghosts were howling.

"Now we are fewer than ever," ghosts were wailing.

Shaman Prince heard no more. For his supernatural helpers were giving him instructions. "Run four times around the chief who pretends to be sick!" they were telling him. "Then kick the ground at his head! And jump back fast!"

Shaman Prince ran four times around the ghost chief. He kicked the ground. And, fortunately, he jumped back very fast. For the earth opened and swallowed up the chief of the ghosts.

The watching ghosts edged fearfully away from Shaman Prince. They did nothing to stop him from going back across the misty bridge, even though he took the ghost medicine regalia with him.

"I am the greatest shaman in the world!" he cried to his four friends when he got back to the village. "The greatest shaman who ever lived." Positively gloating in the crown of dead-men's ribs and the clattering fringe of human bones, he planned greater feats. There was no end to his ambition.

"You go too far, Sea-Hawk," Little Wolf told him; but he got no response.

The two were traveling together when they came to the place where a crowd of people stood weeping on a riverbank.

"What has happened?" Little Wolf asked.

"Our princess has drowned," they answered. "Our head chief's only daughter." And they pointed sadly to the river that raged along between its banks, swollen by the autumn rains.

"Find her body!" Shaman Prince commanded.

"And I will bring her back to life."

It was spring before they found her. When they did, the princess was just a skeleton caught by a branch at the bank of the river. But they picked up the bones, laid them out carefully on a plank by the fire, and sent for Shaman Prince.

"You can't do this," Little Wolf told him. "She has been dead so long that she is happily settled in Ghost Town with her relatives, and with the young man who went over the bridge, too, while he was searching for her body. You can't bring her back."

"I can. And I will," Shaman Prince answered with flashing eyes. "Watch me!" And he started at once for her village.

Little Wolf watched the wild-eyed young man put on the gruesome crown of dead-men's ribs and the gruesome dancing apron that clattered with dead-men's bones. He watched him shake the skull and backbone rattle as he leaned an ear this way, and that way, to listen to his supernatural helpers. Then he watched him sprinkle warm ashes along the dead princess's bones four times.

And then he gasped. For the ashes had turned into flesh and skin.

But there was no life in the beautiful body.

Shaman Prince picked up his white eagle tail. The tribe seemed to hold its breath.

He fanned the cold flesh; and, suddenly, the princess breathed.

He had brought the princess back to life. Her grateful father lavished slaves on Shaman Prince, and canoes, and sea-otter robes, and costly coppers, and exquisitely carved mountain goat-horn spoons. . . .

But the gentle princess only looked about her in a vague, sad way. Then she turned yearning eyes toward Ghost Town, where her aunts and the young man who had gone over the bridge to be with her in the other world would be searching for her. And people edged away from her, though they did not know quite why.

"He has gone too far," Little Wolf said to his three other lifelong friends. "He is ruining life in the villages."

"He has gone too far," other shamans said to one another. No one was calling on them to cure a sick relative, with their powerful plants and their powerful songs and dances. He was ruining the profession of medicine. So they decided to trap him and kill him. They would invite him to a feast of shamans. And they would feed him a bit of dried human flesh —the most dangerous of all things to a doctor.

Shaman Prince received the invitation. And though his supernatural helpers warned him of what would happen, he decided to go. He would use the other shamans' jealousy to perform the greatest shamanistic feat the world had ever seen. He would die and bring himself back to life.

So he went to the feast of shamans. He ate the

bit of dried human flesh. Then, at midnight, when he began to feel sick, he called in all his relatives. "The shamans have fed me dried human flesh," he said. And the people caught their breath before they turned to glare at all the other shamans.

"I am going to die," Shaman Prince went on. "But after I have been dead for a year, I will come back to life . . . if . . ." he glanced about him with his wild eyes, "if one of you will come and stand under my coffin to catch me." Now his voice thundered at them. "If you should fail to stand under my coffin and catch me, if you should be afraid of me, none of you shall be left. Now, who will volunteer to catch me?"

People shrank back. Shamans cowered. And Little Wolf clenched his fists and clamped his mouth shut. He would not help his old friend in this final madness.

"Who will volunteer to catch me?"

"I will catch you," a young voice called. And the people gasped.

It was Raven's Wing, the young prince who was heir now, in Sea-Hawk's place.

Sea-Hawk's eyes flashed. "My ghost medicine regalia!" he commanded; and his four lifelong friends brought it to him. When he had put on the crown of dead-men's ribs and the apron that clattered with a fringe of dead-men's bones, he ran around the fire four times, shaking his skull and backbone rattle.

"Now. My coffin!" he commanded. And his four lifelong friends brought in a cedar box.

He lay down in it, still in his ghostly regalia. And he died at once.

People lit their torches and followed his coffin along the trail that twisted through the dark drooping cedars and past the firs that stood silent in the silence of a world hushed by deep, deep green mosses. They made a ring of flame around an empty grave tree and kept a terrified silence while the new coffin was hoisted up into the tree and secured there.

Raven's Wing shivered. He swallowed and licked his dry lips.

Little Wolf laid a hand on the boy's shoulder. "It will be a year before you must stand under the coffin," he reminded the young prince. "In the meantime, I and my friends will stand watch every night to see that no animal touches him. . . ." Or no angry ghost, he thought.

Night after night after night, Sea-Hawk's four faithful old friends stood watch, two by two, in the ghostly graveyard. And the year passed.

"It was a good year," Little Wolf said to his friends.

Many of the haunting gray people had gone back to Ghost Town. And no one had tried to restore them to life again. In fact, when another woman had died, her relatives had quickly comforted one another by saying, "She is not dead. She has just gone over the bridge and is being warmly welcomed by all the relatives who have gone before her."

"But the year is up tonight," Little Wolf added grimly. "And who knows what will happen if Sea-Hawk can bring himself back to life?"

The whole village was clearly as uneasy as Little Wolf was. And when evening came, many people slipped silently along the trail behind Raven's Wing.

Owls flitted like ghosts among the dark, drooping cedars and the shadowy fir trees; and, like ghosts, they made no sound in their passing.

The graveyard was chill and black with shadows. Mists wreathed among the grave trees and mortuary poles as though a tribe of ghosts, too, had come to see what was going to happen. People were silent.

Suddenly, there was a noise in the coffin.

Raven's Wing shuddered. And Little Wolf laid a firm hand on his shoulder. He urged the boy gently forward, toward the awful grave tree.

The coffin lid opened.

People gasped. Then they stood very still. All eyes were on the coffin.

A queer, warped, ugly owl flew out of the coffin and perched on its edge. It glared down at the gathered people with big, burning yellow eyes fixed immovably in their sockets.

A few people sank to the ground, terrified. Others pulled their blankets tightly about them to control their trembling. Little Wolf firmed his grasp on the boy's shoulder.

"I . . . I promised to catch him," Raven's Wing whispered, readying his arms as if to catch the fearsome bird. He edged closer to the grave tree. He was almost under the coffin when he dared to glance up into the awful, burning, immovable owl eyes. He stopped, terrified. And the owl swooped down at him with a blood-curdling shriek.

The boy sank to the ground, faint with fright.

The grotesque owl glided back up to perch again on the edge of the coffin. And now he spoke. In the voice of Shaman Prince.

"You were afraid of me. All of you. So not one of you will be left. Not one of the shamans who killed me. I will take all of you to Ghost Town, where I am chief now. The ghosts have made me their chief. You will all be my ghosts. And the shamans will be my slaves. For they killed me."

The queer, warped, ugly owl rotated its head to fix its awful eyes on everyone in the graveyard. "I will spare only the four friends who were my lifelong companions, the four friends who have kept faithful watch over me every night since I died. To them, I will leave my supernatural powers. And I will help them to become great shamans." With that, the queer, warped, ugly owl fell back into the coffin. And the lid fell shut.

The graveyard was chill and silent and black with shadows. Only the cold mists moved, wreathing away

186

from the grave trees and the mortuary poles as if the ghosts were returning to their own land.

People looked fearfully at one another. Then, when nothing happened, they fled back along the trail to the village. Nothing happened.

The night passed, and the morning came. But still nothing happened.

"I am going to the burial ground," Little Wolf announced in a clear, firm voice; and he started along the trail. His three friends fell in silently behind him. And, one by one, other people crept along behind them. They stayed well back on the edges of the graveyard while Little Wolf climbed boldly up the grave tree, but their eyes were on him while he opened the coffin. They caught his surprised gasp and his look of astonishment. For there was nothing in the coffin except masses of eagle down.

"The sacred pledge of peace!" Little Wolf cried out to them, dipping his hands into the eagle down to waft it over the graveyard.

"Perhaps we will not die," people whispered to one another.

"Sooner or later we will all die," Little Wolf called out, as though he had heard them. He wafted more eagle down over the frightened people. "And some of us will die a second death in the River of Boiling Oil so that there will always be plenty of Salmon People, and plenty of salmon in the rivers." He blew yet more eagle down over them; and it drifted on them like soft snow. It clung to their dark hair as they made their way back along the trail that twisted through the dark, drooping cedars and past the firs that stood silent in the silence of a world hushed by deep, deep, green mosses.

Then the shamans began to die, one by one, the shamans who had killed Shaman Prince. And the four new young shamans told the people that the new chief of the ghosts had dropped his slave shamans into the River of Boiling Oil to let them move swiftly on into useful, exciting lives as Salmon People.

Then, one by one, people began to die, the people who had gone into the graveyard. But no one asked to have them restored to life. Instead, relatives comforted one another as they had in the old days. They said, "They're not dead. They've merely gone over the bridge to live with all the loving relatives who have gone there before them."

Little Wolf saw how the old ease came back to the village with the old acceptance of life and death. "And things go well now in Ghost Town," he assured the people. "Sea-Hawk is a great chief in that other world that has called to him all his life."

Then Raven's Wing died. And Little Wolf, remembering the valiant little fellow, brought him back to life at once with the help of the new ghost chief and the help of his three friends.

Word of this feat raced along the river. And when a prince died in another village, the chief there sent for the four young shamans. He offered them slaves and canoes and sea-otter robes and costly coppers and carved food chests and exquisitely carved mountain goat-horn spoons if they would restore the prince to life.

"Your prince has been dead four days," Little Wolf protested when they reached the sorrowing village. "And the new chief of the ghosts has forbidden us to restore life to anyone who has been dead for four days." He turned sadly away and went back to his own village to work over a sick woman.

But the three other young medicine men lingered, tempted by the slaves and canoes and sea-otter robes and costly coppers and carved food chests and exquisitely carved mountain goat-horn spoons.

"He is scarcely over the four days," they told one another. The odor of death had scarcely touched his body. "We'll bring his soul back to his body," they told the sorrowing chief.

And when they had ordered the people to sing and sing, and beat on the hollow cedar planks and on the skin drums, they lay down near the dead prince and went into a trance. Their souls left their bodies to go to Ghost Town to find the soul of the dead prince.

Instead, they found the chief of the ghosts. He was waiting for his old friends in front of the great, gossamer house where the new young ghost was being cared for by ghost aunts and ghost uncles and fond old grandfathers and grandmothers.

"You have a bad smell," the Ghost Chief said, waving the three young shamans angrily away from him. "So I know that you have disobeyed my orders about the four days. You will not return to your people. You will stay here with me now."

Back in the sorrowing chief's house, the people sang and sang and sang. They beat and beat and beat on the hollow cedar planks and on the skin drums. But nothing happened. The souls of the three young medicine men did not come back to their bodies. By and by, their three hearts stopped beating, as the prince's heart had stopped. So the chief sent for Little Wolf.

"Take your prince to your burial ground," Little Wolf told the sorrowing chief. "Set the emblems of your family like a fort around him. And remember that he is not really dead. He has merely gone on to the land of ghosts to live with all the loving relatives who have gone there before him."

The chief and his people did this.

And hearts grew easy again in the villages all along the river.

"The laws of life are good," people said to one another.

PEOPLE WHO SAVED THE OLD STORIES FOR THE NEW STORYTELLERS

When white men first arrived on the Northwest Coast with awesome ships, terrifying guns, and an arrogant assumption of superiority, the Indians were deeply shocked.

Like other Stone Age peoples suddenly confronted with their own technological backwardness, they lost confidence in all their old ways—ways developed to meet the particular needs of their particular situation. In the familiar tragedy of culture contact, the young especially hurried to "get out of the blanket." They turned impatient backs on the old stories and the old art that had grown with the stories.

Daily reminders of the old stories began vanishing from sight as the tragedy developed. Even the unique totem poles were being chopped down by people caught in the shame of being "heathen" and "savage," of "worshiping graven images."

Finally, white men's laws banning the potlatch seemed the death blow to the old tales. For, without these great formal gatherings, without these brilliantly staged festivals of the arts of the Northwest Coast, how could the young ever be caught up in the spell of the old tribal myths and legends?

Almost in panic, great museums rushed scholars to the Northwest Coast to record a unique native culture before it could vanish completely. With the help of interpreters, famous ethnologists collected stories. But by now, the turn of this century, the tales had lost their most potent magic. Too, there was the barrier of language. Sometimes there was another factor; for even the most sensitive ethnologists could offend the Indians. And when this happened, the latter sometimes misled the scholars to make them appear ridiculous, to lead them to make statements that even the most shamed Indian could laugh at.

Nevertheless, the stories *were* collected, with care and diligence. They were saved for generations more appreciative of the values and the wisdom of the old Indian tribes.

One such collection is the basic source of the tales in *Once More Upon a Totem* and in the earlier *Once Upon a Totem*. This collection by Prof. Franz Boas was printed in the *Thirty-First Annual Report of the*

Bureau of American Ethnology to the Secretary of the Smithsonian Institution 1909–1910 under the title of *Tsimshian Mythology*. Its tales had been recorded over a period of twelve years by "Mr. Henry W. Tate, of Port Simpson, British Columbia, in Tsimshian, his native language."

No doubt "Mr. Henry W. Tate" was the "white nickname" of a gifted informant who must have been known to his own people by an honored Tsimshian name. For it was the traders' ledgers and the missionaries' church rolls that were best served by European-style family naming.

Naturally, the tales he recorded had been intended for native ears. They had been intended for listeners who belonged to the Northwest Coast and to its unique culture. Who knew all the whys behind the actions.

Such tales need to be reworked for people of a different time, place, and culture—for listeners who are not familiar with the region or its values. So the new storytellers have much to do.

They must change the old text sufficiently to make it really come to life for people who do not know the region, the old culture, or the whys behind the action. Yet they must keep the new text deeply true to the old story.

To do this, they need a genuine familiarity with the Northwest Coast and its native people. They need years of sensitive contact with Indian homes and remote Indian villages to round out the research they can do in archives and in Northwest collections.

They need illustrators as dedicated as themselves to depicting the culture authentically.

Perhaps, most of all, they need readers with understanding hearts and lively imaginations.

Christie Harris started her writing career when she was a young teacher and pursued it avidly while rearing five children in a British Columbia border town. Both her western surroundings and her family became grist for her writing mill. Three of her children lent their life histories to *You Have to Draw the Line Somewhere, Confessions of a Toe-Hanger,* and *Let X Be Excitement.* Northwest Coast Indians and Western Canada provided material for *Once Upon a Totem, West With the White Chiefs, Forbidden Frontier,* and for *Raven's Cry,* a story of the Haida Indians that received the Book of the Year medal from the Canadian Association of Children's Librarians. A combination of grandchildren and Indian lore produced *Secret in the Stalalakum Wild.* One book, *Figleafing Through History: The Dynamics of Dress,* was written with her oldest daughter, Moira Johnston.